Family History on the Web

an internet directory for England & Wales
2008-2009 Edition

Stuart A. Raymond

THE FAMILY HISTORY PARTNERSHIP

Published by:
The Family History Partnership
P.O.Box 502, Bury, Lancashire, BL8 9EP, U.K.
Email: sales@thefamilyhistorypartnership.com
Webpage: **www.thefamilyhistorypartnership.com**

in association with:
S.A. & M.J. Raymond

Email: samjraymond@btopenworld.com
Webpage: **www.stuartraymond.co.uk**

ISBNs:
Family History Partnership: 978 1 906280 05 5
S.A. & M.J. Raymond 978 1 899668 51 9

First published 2001
Second edition 2002
Third edition 2003
Fourth edition 2006
Fifth edition 2008

Printed and bound at the Alden Press, De Havilland Way, Witney, Oxon OX29 0YG

Contents

Introduction   4

1. Gateways, Search Engines, etc.   5

2. General Introductions to Genealogy   7

3. Libraries & Record Offices   10

4. Family History Societies   21

5. Discussion Groups: Mailing Lists, Newsgroups & Message Boards   27

6. County Pages   32

7. Surnames   42

8. Sources   47

9. Occupational Information   80

10. Miscellaneous Sites   101

11. Professional Services, Booksellers, etc   113

Subject Index   118

Institution Index   121

Place Index   126

Introduction

A vast amount of information concerning genealogy and family history is available on the internet. Surfing the net can be a very productive process for the researcher; it can, however, also be very frustrating. Despite the fact that there are thousands of genealogical web sites worth visiting, the means for finding particular relevant sites are very poor: search engines frequently list dozens of irrelevant sites, but not the ones you require. This book is intended to help you identify those sites which are most likely to be relevant to your research. The listing is selective; I have only included those sites which are of general interest to most genealogists. Consequently, I have excluded most sites devoted solely to particular families or particular towns and villages. I have also not listed the innumerable sites which are, in theory, international in scope, but in practice are primarily of interest to American genealogists. I have also excluded those sites which are of general, rather than specifically genealogical interest, e.g. general search engines, map sites, etc. Many of the sites which I have listed can be used to find these excluded categories. Some of the other volumes in this series list many transcripts and indexes of parish registers, monumental inscriptions, war memorials, *etc.,* from particular places.

Beginners should also consult the companion volume: RAYMOND, STUART A. *Netting your ancestors: tracing family history on the internet.* Family History Partnership, 2007. This book offers many suggestions which will improve your surfing techniques.

This listing is as up to date as I have been able to make it. However, new web pages are being mounted all the time, and URLs frequently change. Consequently, this directory will need frequent updating. If you are unable to find a site listed here, then you should check Cyndis List or one of the other gateways listed in chapter 1 below; the probability is that the site has moved to another address. Alternatively, use a search engine such as **www.google.com** to search for the title of the site as given below. If you know of sites which have not been included here, please let me know so that they can be included in the next edition of this directory.

My thanks go to Cynthia Hanson, who has typed most of this book, to Bob Boyd, who has seen it through the press, and to partners of the Family History Partnership for their continued support.

Stuart A. Raymond

1. Gateways, Search Engines, etc.

There are a variety of gateways and search engines for English genealogists. The most useful is probably Genuki, which itself provides a great deal of information, and has links to numerous other pages. Cyndis List is the major international gateway. It has an American bias, but nevertheless provides links to thousands of UK sites. Quite a number of other sites offer similar help, although the international sites tend to be biased towards U.S. genealogy. General search engines are not listed here; they may be found on Cyndis List, or by accessing some of the other sites listed below.

- Genuki
  www.genuki.org.uk
  This site contains over 60,000 pages of structured information.
- Genuki Book by David Hawgood
  www.hawgood.co.uk/genuki/index.htm
  A useful description of Genuki contents
- Cyndis List
  www.cyndislist.com
  The most extensive listing of genealogical websites on the net. Over 260,000 links
- Roots Web
  www.rootsweb.com/
  Home to thousands of genealogical mailing lists, the Gen Web project, web sites, *etc.* American bias, but also much of interest to English researchers
- Archives Portal: Projects, Resources and Initiatives
  www.nationalarchives.gov.uk/portal
  Gateway to major resources
- BIGenealogy: British Isles Genealogy
  www.bigenealogy.com/
  Gateway

- British Isles Genweb Project
  www.britishislesgenweb.org/
  Important for its county sites; see below, chapter 6
- Bob Holloway's Genealogy Page for Source Information
  members.aol.com/aisling13/
  General guide to UK sites
- British Isles Genealogy
  genealogy.about.com/od/british_isles
- Family Records Portal
  www.familyrecords.gov.uk
  Links.to the websites of all the major national repositories
- Finding Genealogy on the Internet
  www.spub.co.uk/fgi/links.html
  Links to numerous search engines, gateways, etc.
- Free Databases for Genealogical Searching
  www.ormond.i8.com
  Links page
- Geneally
  www.geneally.com
  Gateway to sites recommended by users
- Genealogy Database.co.uk
  www.genealogydatabase.co.uk
- Genealogy Links
  www.genealogylinks.net/
  The U.K. section has over 8,000 links
- Genealogy-Links
  www.genealogy-links.co.uk
  Gateway
- The Genealogists Internet
  www.spub.co.uk/tgi3/links.php
  Gateway to sites listed in Peter Christian's book
- Genealogy on the Internet
  www.geocities.com/Heartland/6266/genealogy.htm
  Discussion of the various types of genealogical sites, with links to 'gateway' sites
- Genealogy Resources on the Internet: United Kingdom Resources
  www-personal.umich.edu/~cgaunt/uk.html
  Gateway site

- Global Information Centre Historical and Genealogical Resources
  www.gic.co.uk/roots.htm
  International links page, with many British entries
- Grahams Genealogy Links
  www.hants.gov.uk/genealogy/
  Links page
- Looking 4 Kin Genealogy Links & Chat
  www.looking4Kin.com/
  Includes many links for English and Welsh counties
- UK & Ireland Genealogy Search
  mygensearch.com/
- The UK Gen Web Site
  www.ukgenweb.com/
  Links site
- UK Genealogy
  www.ukgenealogy.co.uk
  Includes county pages
- Web Sites for Genealogists: an Australian gateway site for tracing your family history
  www.coraweb.com.au/index.htm
  Lists some U.K. sites

For those with historical interests, it may be useful to visit:
- Internet Resources for Historians: United Kingdom
  www.hist.unt.edu/web__resources/uk.htm

For search engines, see:
- Search Engines
  www.cyndislist.com/search.htm
- FEEFHS Top Internet Search Engines that can find Genealogy Stuff
  feefhs.org/WEBM/SESEARCH.HTML
- Gendoor
  www.gendoor.com
  Subject specific search engine
- Geneanet: Genealogical Database Network
  www.geneaseek.org
  Genealogical search engine

- Gensource I Found It: the genealogy web directory exclusively for genealogists
  www.gensource.com/ifoundit/
  Search engine
- Nedgen Genealogy Searchengine
  www.nedgen.com
- Top Search Engines and Directories: Genealogy and Family History Internet Portals and Browsers
  www.academic-genealogy.com/topsearchenginesdirectories.htm
- Yahoo UK Genealogy Links
  uk.dir.yahoo.com/Arts/Humanities/History/Genealogy

General search techniques are discussed in:
- Finding Your Ancestors on the Internet: advanced genealogy search techniques
  genealogy.about.com/library/weekly/aa041700e.htm

If you are searching Google for particular ancestors, consult:
- Free Genealogy Search Help for Google
  www.genealogy-search-help.com

See also:
- Googling Genealogy Style: Twelve Google Search Tips for Genealogists
  genealogy.about.com/library/weekly/aao52902a.htm

For means of sharing your research on Rootsweb, consult:
- Share Your Family History
  searches.rootsweb.com/share.html

Webrings link together sites on a common theme. For genealogical webrings, see:
- United Kingdom Genealogy Webring
  www.accessgenealogy.com/rings/uk.htm

For some useful guidance on using the internet, consult:
- Researching your Roots Using the Internet / Cyndi Howells
  www.familychronicle.com/internet.html

By the time you consult this directory, some of the sites listed are likely to have been removed from the internet. It is nevertheless possible that copies of these pages have been archived at:
- Wayback Machine
  www.archive.org

2. General Introductions to Genealogy

Numerous general guides to English genealogy are available on the internet; most provide much the same basic guidance. Many family history society web sites (chapter 4 below) have beginners guides; so do many of the county pages listed in chapter 6. Pages from some of the major institutions *etc.,* include:

- A-Z of British Genealogical Research
  www.genuki.org.uk/big/EmeryPaper.html
- BIFHS-U.S.A. Guide to British Isles Research
  www.rootsweb.com/~bifhsusa/research.html
- British-Genealogy.com
  www.british-genealogy.com
  Introductory pages on a range of topics
- Encyclopedia of Genealogy
  www.eogen.com
  User contribution site; with a U.S. bias at present, but likely to expand
- England Genealogy: Tracing Your English Ancestors
  genealogy.about.com/od/england/
- England Research Outline
  www.familysearch.org
  Click 'search', 'research helps', 'E' (for England), and scroll down to title
- Family History: your guide to resources
  www.nationalarchives.gov.uk/familyhistory/
  From The National Archives
- Explore Genealogy
  www.exploregenealogy.co.uk
- Family History in England and Wales
  www.nationalarchives.gov.uk/catalogue/researchguidesindex.asp
  Click title

- Family History
  www.bbc.co.uk/history/familyhistory/
  From the B.B.C. Includes video guides to sources
- Family History Workshop with Steve Jacques
  members.lycos.co.uk/familyhistory2/FamilyHistoryWorkshop.htm
  'How to' guide
- Research Tips: First Steps in Family History
  www.ffhs.org.uk/tips/first.php
  From the Federation of Family History Societies
- Frequently Asked Questions: the answers according to GENUKI
  www.cs.ncl.ac.uk/genuki/faq.html
- Gendocs: Genealogical Research in England & Wales
  www.gendocs.demon.co.uk/
- Genealogy helper: tracing UK ancestors
  www.jaydax.co.uk/genlinks
  Introductory pages
- Genealogy and Family History Research in U.K.
  homepages.nildram.co.uk/~jimella/geneal3.htm
- Getting Started in Genealogy and Family History
  www.genuki.org.uk/gs/
- History Trails: Family History
  www.bbc.co.uk/history/trail/familyhistory/
  Introductory guide from the B.B.C.
- Introduction to Genealogy Research for the United Kingdom
  genealogypro.com/articles/genealogy-research-uk-1.html
- Newbie's Guide to Genealogy and Family History, by
  Roy Stockdill
  www.genuki.org.uk/gs/Newbie.html
- Notes for Americans on Tracing their British Ancestry
  www.sog.org.uk/leaflets/americans.pdf
- Researching Ancestors from the United Kingdom using the LDS
  Family History Center's Resources
  www.oz.net/~markhow/uksearch.htm
- Researching From Abroad
  www.genuki.org.uk/ab/
- Researching Your Family History
  www.bl.uk/collections/wider/pdf/researchfamhist.pdf
  From the British Library

- Rootsweb Guide to Tracing Family Trees
  www.rootsweb.com/~rwguide/lesson28.htm
  Includes English and Welsh research
- Starting Genealogy
  www.sog.org.uk/leaflets/starting.html
  From the Society of Genealogists
- UK Genealogy
  www.ukgenealogy.co.uk
  General guidance, including numerous county pages, search
  engine, *etc.*
- What is Genealogy?
  www.genuki.org.uk/gs/Bunting.html

For medieval genealogy, see:
- Medieval and Early Modern Sources for Family History
  www.nationalarchives.gov.uk/catalogue/researchguidesindex.asp
  Click title (under 'Family History')
- Some Notes on Medieval English Genealogy
  www.medievalgenealogy.org.uk
  Many pages

Despite the internet, books continue to be crucial to the family
historian. Many genealogical books are identified and located by:
- Google Book Search
  books.google.com/

See also:
- Google Book Search: Hints and Tips
  www.medievalgenealogy.org.uk/google.shtml

There is a notable lack of good genealogical bibliographies on the
internet. The only general site of any value - although now rather
outdated - is:
- Sources for Research in English Genealogy
  www.loc.gov/rr/genealogy/bib_guid/england.html
  Bibliographic guide from the Library of Congress

The most important bibliography on the web for genealogists is:
- Texts and Calendars since 1982: a survey
  www.rhs.ac.uk/textsandcals.htm
  This is the online update of MULLINS, E.L.C. *Texts and calendars: an analytical guide to serial publications.* Royal Historical Society, 1978; supplement 1983, which lists the innumerable editions and indexes of original documents such as wills, deeds, eclesiastical records, *etc., etc.,* published by record societies.

See also:
- Texts and Calendars: a guide to holdings in York
  www.york.ac.uk/services/library/publications/guides/textcal.htm

The authoritative series of bibliographies for English genealogy are listed at:
- British Genealogical Library Guides
  www.stuartraymond.co.uk
  Click title

Many thousand historical works (a large number of which could be useful to the genealogist) are listed in:
- Royal Historical Society bibliography
  www.rhs.ac.uk/bibl/

Comprehensive online metropolitan and county bibliographies, with much of interest to the genealogist, are provided by:
- Historical Books about the Weald of Kent, Surrey and Sussex
  thesussexweald.org/hbooks.asp
  A virtual library, including several trade directories
- Tameside Bibliography
  www.tameside.gov.uk/leisure/new/lh23.htm
  Click title
- Hertfordshire Archive
  www.hertfordshire-archive.co.uk
  Digital archive of past publications
- Foster Library Bibliographies
  www.lincolnshire.gov.uk/section.asp?sectionType=28catId=6684
  Lincolnshire bibliography

- London's Past Online: A bibliography of London history
  www.rhs.ac.uk/bibl/London.asp
- Bibliography
  www.staffshistory.org.uk/bibliography.htm
  For Staffordshire
- Suffolk Bibliography
  content.ancestry.com/iexec/?htx=BookList&dbid=7529
  Subscription required. Originally published 1979
- The Sussex Historians Handbook, compiled by John H. Farrant
  www.sussexpast.co.uk/research/
  Click title
- Bibliography of Cardiganshire 1600-1959
  www.ceredigion.gov.uk/index.cfm?articleid=3610
  Scroll down and click page required

See also:
- Clive Smith's UK Genealogy Homepage
  ourworld.compuserve.com/homepages/Clive_Smith
  List of a library of books on genealogy, *etc.*

Welsh genealogy is considered separately in:
- Digging up your Roots in Wales
  www.genuki.org.uk/big/wal/wales.html
- Wales: Research Outline
  www.familysearch.org
  Click 'search', 'research helps', 'W' (for Wales), and scroll down to title

It is important to check that the research you intend to do has not already been done. On this, see:
- Has it been done before?
  www.sog.org.uk/leaflets/done.pdf
  How to find completed research
- England: How to Find Family Histories
  www.familysearch.org/
  Click 'search', 'research helps', 'E' (for England), and scroll down to title

3. Libraries and Record Offices

Despite the huge quantity of genealogical information now available on the internet, genealogists will continue to rely heavily on printed books and archival materials for most of their research. The libraries and record offices which hold these resources will continue to provide an essential service. Many of them now have web-pages, listed here. Those institutions which provide internet access to searchable catalogues and indexes, *etc.,* are providing a particularly valuable service.

Libraries
It is impossible here to provide a complete list of library websites which may be of use to genealogists. Such a list would have to include most public and many university library sites, and is outside the scope of this book. However, a number of sites provide extensive listings. These include:
- FAMILIA: the UK and Ireland's Guide to Genealogical Resources in Public Libraries
  www.familia.org.uk
  Extensive listing of genealogical resources, of particular value for its notes on the holdings etc. of particular libraries
- OPACS in Britain and Ireland
  **www.hero.ac.uk/reference__and__subject__resources/
  opacs__in__britain__and__ireland__3795.cfm**
  Directory of library catalogues and services in Britain and Ireland, maintained by NISS
- BUBL Information Service
  bubl.ac.uk
  Click 'BUBL UK' and 'Libraries' for UK national public and university libraries, including list of University library catalogues on-line
- COPAC Academic and National Library Catalogue
  www.copac.ac.uk
  Union catalogue of 27 major university and national libraries
- Libdex: the library index
  www.libdex.com/
  Lists thousands of library catalogues worldwide
- UK Public Libraries
  dspace.dial.pipex.com/town/square/ac940/ukpublib.html
  Lists public libraries on the web, including those with on-line catalogues
- Libraries Archives & Museums Index
  www.CyndisList.com/libes.htm

Archives
Numerous record offices also have a web presence. Typically, these sites include details of access, opening hours, services, and collections. Some provide an overwhelming amount of information, and I have tried to indicate this in the listing below. There are a number of gateways and on-line listings. These include:
- Archon
  www.nationalarchives.gov.uk/archon
  The authoritative listing of British record repositories, arranged alphabetically and including many libraries and museums who hold archives. Includes URLs where available, with basic details of holdings.
- Family Records.gov.uk
  www.familyrecords.gov.uk
  Gateway to major national archives
- English Record Offices and Archives on the Web
  www.oz.net/~markhow/englishros.htm
  Gateway to the web, arranged by county. Primarily county record offices.

There are two important union catalogues of archive collections:
- A2A: Access to Archives
  www.a2a.org.uk
  Catalogues from 414 English record offices, listing over 16,000,000 records
- Archives Hub
  www.archiveshub.ac.uk
  Gateway to the archives held by UK universities and colleges

Other useful sites include:
- Archives Portal
  www.portal.nationalarchives.gov.uk/
  Gateway to archival projects
- County Archives Research Network
  www.suffolk.gov.uk/LeisureAndCulture/LocalHistoryAndHeritage/
  SuffolkRecordOffice/HowToUseTheSuffolkRecordOffice/
  LeafletsandResourceLists.htm
  Click title. Useful information on CARN readers tickets, now required for admission to many record offices.

Those about to visit a record office for the first time should read:
- Archival Research Techniques and Skills
  www.arts-scheme.co.uk/

National and International Institutions

British Library
- British Library
  www.bl.uk
  Houses one of the largest collections of genealogical books and manuscripts, etc., in the UK. Particularly important pages are listed separately below.
- British Library Integrated catalogue
  catalogue.bl.uk
- British Library Manuscripts Catalogues
  www.bl.uk/catalogues/manuscripts.html
- British Library Newspaper Collections
  www.bl.uk/collections/collect.html
- British Library: India Office Records
  www.bl.uk/collections/orientaloffice.html

National Archives
- The National Archives
  www.nationalarchives.gov.uk
  The major British archive repository. Access to catalogue of over 10,000,000 documents, and much, much more!

- The National Archives: Research Guides
  www.nationalarchives.gov.uk/catalogue/researchguidesindex.asp
  Invaluable series of guides, many of which are separately listed elsewhere in this directory
- Family Records Centre
  www.familyrecords.gov.uk/frc/
  For post-1837 births, marriages and deaths, census returns, and wills, *etc.* Now closed, but check for details of alternative arrangements.
- National Register of Archives
  www.nationalarchives.gov.uk/nra
  Includes access to database index of manuscript collections throughout the UK
- The List and Index Society
  www.listandindexsociety.org.uk
  Publishers of calendars and indexes of documents in The National Archives

Latter Day Saints
- FamilySearch
  www.familysearch.org
  Web site for the Latter Day Saints Library in Utah. Extensive, including the I.G.I., the library's catalogue, a list of family history centres in the U.K., and many pages of 'research helps'
- Steve's Quick Guide to the www.familysearch.org web site
  members.lycos.co.uk/familyhistory2/fs.htm
- LDS & Family History Centers
  www.cyndislist.com/lds.htm
- Roots-L Resources: Family History Centers and Library
  www.rootsweb.com/roots-l/fhc.html
- LDS Information
  www.genuki.org.uk/big/LDS/
  Addresses of UK family history centers, with description of their catalog
- Hyde Park Family History Centre
  www.hydeparkfhs.org
  Includes list of UK family history centres

Specialist Institutions
- Bethlem Royal Hospital Archives and Museum
  www.bethlemheritage.org.uk

- BT Group Archives
  www.btplc.com/Thegroup/BTsHistory/BTgrouparchives/
  The collection includes an almost complete set of phone directories
- College of Arms
  www.college-of-arms.gov.uk/
- The British Postal Museum & Archive
  www.postalheritage.org.uk
- Library of the Religious Society of Friends in Britain
  www.quaker.org.uk/
  Click 'The Library' and 'Genealogy' for a guide to Quaker genealogical sources
- Huguenot Library: University College London
  www.ucl.ac.uk/Library/huguenot.shtml
- Imperial War Museum
  www.iwm.org.uk
  Includes detailed list of manuscript collections; also pages on the National Inventory of War Memorials, and on family history research, *etc.*
- Lambeth Palace Library
  www.lambethpalacelibrary.org
  Very detailed guide to archives of the Archbishops of Canterbury
- Leicester University Dept. of English Local History
  www.le.ac.uk/elh/
- The Library and Museum of Freemasonry
  freemasonry.london.museum
- Methodist Archives and Research Centre
  www.library.manchester.ac.uk/specialcollections/methodist/
  Online guides include 'Methodist Archives Biographical Index', 'Researching your Family History', 'index of ministers', *etc.*
- Modern Records Centre
  www2.warwick.ac.uk/services/library/mrc/
  Includes detailed 'subject guides', including a guide to Family History at the Modern Records Centre'.
- Museum of English Rural Life
  www.ruralhistory.org
  Includes list of manuscripts and online book catalogue
- National Army Museum
  www.national-army-museum.ac.uk/

- National Maritime Museum
  www.nmm.ac.uk
  Includes online manuscripts catalogue
- The parliamentary Archives
  www.parliament.uk/parliamentary_publications_and_archives/
  parliamentary_archives.cfm
- Society of Antiquaries of London
  www.sal.org.uk
- Dr. Williams Library
  www1.rhbnc.ac.uk/hellenic-institute/Drwilliams's.html
  Brief guide to a nonconformist collection

University Libraries
Most university library catalogues are available on the internet, and their addresses can be found on the gateway sites listed above. A full listing cannot be given here, although it should be emphasised that university libraries frequently hold many books, journals, microfilm, *etc.,* of genealogical interest. The sites listed below are included here because of special features other than their book catalogues. This is a very select list; genealogists should always visit the websites of universities in their ancestral home areas, to see whether they hold any archives or special collections relevant to their research.

- University of Birmingham Special Collections
  www.special-coll.bham.ac.uk
  Includes the archives of the Church Missionary Society
- Cambridge University Library
  www.lib.cam.ac.uk
  Copyright deposit library; extensive manuscript collection, including Ely Diocesan Archives.
- Durham University Library. Heritage Collections
  www.dur.ac.uk/library/asc/
  Includes handlists of a wide range of collections, including Durham Diocesan archives, and many estate archives *etc.*
- Family Archives at Durham University Library
  familyrecords.dur.ac.uk
- University of Hull Archives
  www.hull.ac.uk/arc/collection/
  Includes detailed listings of collections of estate papers, business records, religious archives, *etc.*

- Keele University Library: Special Collections and Archives
  www.keele.ac.uk/depts/li/specarc/
  The library holds a good local collection of Staffordshire books; archives include Tamworth court rolls, the Wedgwood archive, Sneyd papers, etc.
- Special Collections at Leeds University Library
  www.leeds.ac.uk/library/spcoll/index.htm
  The library has an extensive collection of books on English local history, especially Yorkshire; also a variety of estate archives, etc.
- Institute of Historical Research, University of London
  ihr.sas.ac.uk/
  Includes extensive guide to the web for historians
- John Rylands University Library of Manchester
  www.library.manchester.ac.uk
  See special collections pages for extensive estate and religious archives
- University of Nottingham Manuscripts and Special Collections
  www.nottingham.ac.uk/mss/
  Holds records of the Archdeaconry of Nottingham, various family and estate collections, *etc*
- Bodleian Library, University of Oxford: Department of Special Collections and Western Manuscripts
  www.bodley.ox.ac.uk/dept/scwmss/
- The Archives of Balliol College University of Oxford
  web.balliol.ox.ac.uk/history/archives/index.asp
- University of Southampton Libraries: Special Collections
  www.archives.lib.soton.ac.uk/
  Includes extensive guide to archive and manuscript collections
- University of Swansea Library Information Services Archives
  www.swan.ac.uk/lis/historicalcollections/Archives
  Includes details of the 'Local Archive Collection' (including Corporation of Swansea records), the 'South Wales Coalfield Collection' *etc.*

COUNTY RECORD OFFICES AND LOCAL HISTORY LIBRARIES

Bedfordshire
- Bedfordshire and Luton Archives and Record Service
  www.bedfordshire.gov.uk/CommunityAndLiving/ ArchivesAndRecordOffice
  Includes extensive guides to sources
- Bedfordshire & Luton Archives & Records Service (BLARS) Holdings
  www.genuki.org.uk/big/eng/BDF/RecordOffice/index.html
  Various unofficial guides to sources

Berkshire
- Berkshire Record Office
  www.berkshirerecordoffice.org.uk

Buckinghamshire
- Centre for Buckinghamshire Studies
  www.buckscc.gov.uk/archives/index.stm

Cambridgeshire
- Cambridgeshire Archives and Local Studies Service
  www.cambridgeshire.gov.uk/leisure/archives/
- Wisbech and Fenland Museum
  www.wisbechmuseum.org.uk
  Includes list of parish registers and other local records held

Cheshire
- Cheshire and Chester Archives and Local Studies
  www.cheshire.gov.uk/recoff/home.htm
- Tameside Local Studies & Archives Centre
  www.tameside.gov.uk/leisure/new/lh23.htm
  Includes page on 'Manchester Regiment Archives on the Boer War'
- Chester History & Heritage
  www.chester.gov.uk/heritage/

Cornwall
- Cornwall Centre / Kresenn Kernow
  www.chycor.co.uk/general/red-lib/
- Cornwall Record Office
  www.cornwall.gov.uk/cro/

- Royal Institution of Cornwall
  www.royalcornwallmuseum.org.uk/
  Click 'R.I.C.', and 'Courtney Library'

Cumberland
- Cumbria Archive Service
  www.cumbria.gov.uk/archives/

Derbyshire
- Derbyshire Record Office
  www.derbyshire.gov.uk/leisure/record_office/

Devon
- Devon Libraries Local Studies Service
  www.devon.gov.uk/etched
  Includes pages on the West Country Studies Library, and other local studies libraries in Barnstaple, Plymouth, Torquay, *etc.* The West Country Studies library houses the library of the Devon and Cornwall Record Society (mainly parish register transcripts). There are also many guides to sources *etc.*
- Devon Record Office
  www.devon.gov.uk/record_office.htm
  Includes lists of parish registers held at Devon Record Office, North Devon Record Office, and Plymouth and West Devon Record Office
- Plymouth & West Devon Record Office
  www.plymouth.gov.uk/archives/
- Plymouth City Council: Local and Naval Studies Library
  www.plymouth.gov.uk/homepage/yourcouncil/
  leisure-4/libraries/findyourlibrary/centrallibrary/
  localstudieslibrary.htm
- Torbay Council Local Studies
  www.torbay.gov.uk/index/leisure/libraries/archives/
  research_service.htm

Dorset
- Dorset History Centre
  www.dorsetforyou.com/index.jsp?articleid=2203

- West Dorset Research Centre: Dorset Migration Local and Family History
  www.dorsetmigration.org.uk

Durham
- Durham County Record Office
  www.durham.gov.uk/recordoffice/usp.nsf
  Includes searchable database of holdings; also detailed information on each parish, and on nonconformist churches
- Gateshead Local Studies: Local and Family History Online
  www.asaplive.com/Local/Home.cfm?Login=Done
- Tyne & Wear Archives Service
  www.tyneandweararchives.org.uk
  Includes many user guides, including lists of parish registers and other sources.

Essex
- Essex Record Office
  www.essexcc.gov.uk/
  Click 'Enjoying Essex' and 'Archives & Museums'. Includes catalogue of archives.
- Newham Archives and Local History
  www.newham.gov.uk/Services/ArchivesandLocalHistory/
- Redbridge Local Studies and Libraries
  www.redbridge.gov.uk/cms/cms/education_and_learning/
  libraries/local_studies_and_archives.aspx
- Vestry House Museum Local Studies Library
  www.lbwf.gov.uk/index/leisure/museums-galleries/
  vestry-house-museum/local-studies-library.htm
  Waltham Forest

Gloucestershire and Bristol
- Gloucestershire County Council: Local Studies
  www.libraries.gloucestershire.gov.uk/index.cfm?articleid=1768
  Includes pages on local studies centres across the county
- Gloucestershire Archives
  archives.gloscc.gov.uk
  www.gloucestershire.gov.uk/index.cfm?articleID=1348
  Site includes a 'genealogical database', indexing wills, nonconformist baptisms, gaol registers, poor law records *etc.*

- Bristol Record Office
  www.bristol.gov.uk/ccm/navigation/leisure-and-culture/
  records-and-archives
  Includes online catalogue.
- Central Library: Family History and Local Studies
  www.bristol.gov.uk/ccm/content/Leisure-Culture/Libraries/
  central-library-family-history-and-local-studies.en
  At Bristol

Hampshire
- Hampshire Record Office
  www.hants.gov.uk/record-office/index.html
- Hantsweb: Local Studies and Family History
  www3.hants.gov.uk/library/local-studies.htm
- Isle of Wight Record Office
  www.iwight.com/library/record__office/
  Includes various databases
- Isle of Wight Record Office
  www.isle-of-wight-fhs.co.uk/recoffic.htm
  (from the Isle of Wight Family History Society site)
- Portsmouth Records Office
  www.portsmouthrecordsoffice.co.uk
- Southampton Online: City Archives
  www.southampton.gov.uk/leisure/history/archives/default.asp
- Southampton Online: Family and Local History
  www.southampton.gov.uk/libraries/family-history

Herefordshire
- Herefordshire Archive Service
  www.herefordshire.gov.uk/leisure/archives/3584.asp

Hertfordshire
- Hertfordshire Archives and Local Studies
  www.hertsdirect.org/libsleisure/heritage1/HALS/

Huntingdonshire
- County Record Office, Huntingdon
  www.cambridgeshire.gov.uk/leisure/archives/visiting/
  crohuntingdon.htm

- Summary of Documentary and Library Holdings in the
  Huntingdon County Record Office
  www.genuki.org.uk/big/eng/HUN/RecordOffice.html
- Cambridgeshire Record Office (Huntingdon): User Information
  www.genuki.org.uk/big/eng/HUN/ROuser.html

Kent
- Kent County Council: Archives and Local History
  www.kent.gov.uk/leisure-and-culture/
  local-history-and-heritage/archives-and-local-history
  Pages for the Centre for Kentish Studies, East Kent Archives
  Centre, Canterbury Cathedral Archives, and 'local history in
  libraries'
- Bexley Local Studies and Archive Centre
  www.bexley.gov.uk/service/lib-localstudies.html
- Bromley Local Studies Library and Archives
  www.bromley.gov.uk/libraries/librariesintheborough/
  Click 'Local Studies and Archives'.
- Greenwich Heritage Centre
  www.greenwich.gov.uk/Greenwich/LeisureCulture/
  HistoryandHeritage/HeritageCentre/

- Lewisham Local Studies and Archives
  www.lewisham.gov.uk/LeisureandCulture/
  LocalHistoryAndHeritage/LocalHistoryAndArchivesCentre
- Medway City Ark
  cityark.medway.gov.uk/

Lancashire
- Lancashire Record Office
  www.lancashire.gov.uk/education/record__office/
- Salford Diocesan Archives
  www.churches-online.org.uk/salfordarchives/
  Roman Catholic archives
- Archives 2002: a guide to the resources of the Bolton Archive and
  Local Studies Unit
  homepage.ntlworld.com/judy.whitby/penmaenucha/history/
  public%20records.htm

- Bury Archives
  www.bury.gov.uk/leisureandculture/libraries/archives/
  default.asp
- Manchester Archives and Local Studies
  www.manchester.gov.uk/libraries/arls/
- Greater Manchester Archives: a guide to local repositories
  www.gmcro.co.uk/guides/gmguide/purple2.htm
  Includes notes on many local record offices
- Greater Manchester County Record Office
  www.gmcro.co.uk
- Oldham Local Studies and Archives
  www.oldham.gov.uk/community/local_studies.htm
  Includes lists of parish registers, monumental inscriptions and
  newspapers, *etc.*
- Rochdale Local Studies Library
  www.rochdale.gov.uk/Leisure_and_Culture/
  local_history_and_heritage/local_studies_library.aspx
- Salford Local History Library
  www.salford.gov.uk/living/yourcom/salfordlife/aboutsalford/
  salfordlocalhistory/lhlibrary
- Stockport Archives
  www.stockport.gov.uk/content/leisureculture/libraries/
  libraryfinder/centrallibrary/archives
  Includes page on 'Manchester Regiment Archives on the Boer War'
- Tameside Local Studies and Archives Centre
  www.tameside.gov.uk/leisure/new/lh23.htm
- Trafford Metropolitan Borough: Local Studies Centre
  www.trafford.gov.uk/LeisureAndCulture/Libraries/
  RecordsAndArchives-LocalStudies
- Warrington Borough Council: Local and Family History
  www.warrington.gov.uk/Leisureandculture/Libraries/
  family_history
- Wigan Archive Service
  www.wlct.org/Culture/Heritage/archives.htm

Leicestershire
- The Record Office for Leicestershire, Leicester and Rutland
  www.leics.gov.uk/record_office.htm

- Leicestershire & Rutland Family History Society: the Record
  Office for Leicestershire, Leicester and Rutland
  lrfhs.org.uk/leicrecoff.html

Lincolnshire
- Lincolnshire Archives
  www.lincolnshire.gov.uk/archives/
  Includes many guides to sources
- Lincolnshire Libraries: Local Studies in Libraries
  www.lincolnshire.gov.uk/section.asp?docId=28154&catId=2057
- North Lincolnshire Council: Local and Family History
  www.northlincs.gov.uk/NorthLincs/Leisure/libraries/
  localandfamilyhistory/

London & Middlesex
- London Repositories and their Collections
  ourworld.compuserve.com/homepages/jkonvalinka/London.htm
- London Boroughs: Archives and Local Studies Libraries
  homepages.gold.ac.uk/genuki/LND/boro-lib.htm
- City of London: Libraries, Archives, Museums & Galleries
  www.cityoflondon.gov.uk/leisure_heritage/
  libraries_archives_museums_galleries/
  Includes pages for Corporation of London Record Office, London
  Metropolitan Archives, and Guildhall Library.
- Guildhall Library Manuscripts Section
  ihr.sas.ac.uk/gh/
  Includes many guides to sources
- Sources for Biographical and Genealogical Research at Guildhall
  Library
  www.history.ac.uk/gh/gene.htm
- Brent Archive
  www.brent.gov.uk/archive
- Camden Local Studies & Archives Centre
  www.camden.gov.uk/ccm/navigation/leisure/local-history/
- Ealing Local History Centre
  www.ealing.gov.uk/services/libraries/
  local_history-centre/index.html
- Enfield Libraries Local History Unit
  www.enfield.gov.uk/448/Local%20History%20Unit.htm
  Click 'Leisure & Culture', 'Libraries', and 'Local History'.

- Hackney Archives
  www.hackney.gov.uk/ca.archives.htm
- Hammersmith & Fulham Libraries - Archives & Local History
  www.lbhf.gov.uk/Directory/Leisure_and_Culture/Libraries/
  Archives
- Haringey Archive Service
  www.haringey.gov.uk/index/community_and_leisure/
  time_out_in_haringey/visiting_haringey/places_to_visit/
  brucecastlemuseum/archives.htm
- Harrow Council Civic Centre Library: Local History Library
  www.harrow.gov.uk/site/scripts/
  documentID=926&pageNumber=3
- Hillingdon Local Studies and Archives
  www.hillingdon.gov.uk/education/library/heritage/index.php
- Hounslow Local Studies and Archives
  www.hounslow.info/libraries.htm
  Click 'Local Studies and Archives'

- Islington Local History Centre
  www.islington.gov.uk/Education/Libraries/Local/
  LocalHistoryCentre.asp
- Royal Borough of Kensington and Chelsea Local Studies and
  Archives
  www.rbkc.gov.uk/libraries/localstudiesandarchives/

- Tower Hamlets Local History & Archives
  www.towerhamlets.gov.uk/data/libraries-leisure/data/libraries/
  history-archive.cfm
- City of Westminster Archives Centre
  www.westminster.gov.uk/libraries/archives/index.cfm
  Detailed 'Archives Guide'.

Norfolk
- Norfolk Record Office
  archives.norfolk.gov.uk/nroindex.htm
  Includes 32 brief 'information leaflets', detailed guide to holdings,
  and lists of the archives of Norwich, Great Yarmouth, and Kings
  Lynn.

Northamptonshire
- Northamptonshire Record Office
  www.northamptonshire.gov.uk/Community/record/
  about_us.htm

Northumberland
- Tracing Your Ancestors in North East England
  www.genuki.bpears.org.uk/NBL/NCLLib/NCLGG2.html
- Northumberland Collections Service
  solar.northumberland.gov.uk/jetspeed/portal
  Go to 'Find a Service', search for 'Collections' and click title
- Northumberland County Council Local Studies Collection
  solar.northumberland.gov.uk/jetspeed/portal/
  Click 'Find a Service' and search 'Local Studies'
- Berwick-upon-Tweed Record Office
  pscm.northumberland.gov.uk/portal/
  page?_pageid=106,54411&dad=portal92&_schema=
  PORTAL92&pid=90043
- Newcastle Local Studies Library
  www.genuki.bpears.org.uk/NBL/NCLLib/
  Genuki page
- North Tyneside Council: Local Studies
  www.northtyneside.gov.uk/newlib/local_studies.htm
- Tyne & Wear Archives Service
  www.tyneandwearachives.org.uk
  Includes many user guides, with an online catalogue

Nottinghamshire
- Nottinghamshire Archives
  www.nottinghamshire.gov.uk/home/leisure/archives.htm

Oxfordshire
- Oxfordshire Studies
  www.oxfordshire.gov.uk/cos/
- Oxfordshire Record Office
  www.oxfordshire.gov.uk/oro

Rutland *see* Leicestershire

Shropshire

- Shropshire Archives
  www.shropshire.gov.uk/archives.nsf
  Includes online catalogue

Somerset

- Somerset Archive and Record Service
  www.somerset.gov.uk/archives/
  Includes Bridgwater crew list database, Ilchester gaol registers index, index to Somerset wills 1812-1857, many guides to sources, and an online catalogue
- Bath Record Office
  www.batharchives.co.uk
  Includes details of the *Bath Chronicle* Georgian newspaper project

Staffordshire

- Staffordshire and Stoke on Trent Archive Services
  www.staffordshire.gov.uk/leisure/archives/
  Includes pages for Staffordshire Record Office, Stoke on Trent City Archives, Lichfield Record Office, the William Salt Library, Stafford, and the Burton Family and Local History Centre
- Walsall Local History Centre
  www.walsall.gov.uk/local_history_centre
- Wolverhampton Archives and Local Studies
  www.wolverhamptonarchives.dial.pipex.com
  Includes many guides to sources, and some transcripts/indexes of registers, *etc.*

Suffolk

- Suffolk Record Office
  www.suffolkcc.gov.uk/LeisureAndCulture/ LocalHistoryandHeritage/SuffolkRecordOffice/
  Covers the offices at Bury St. Edmunds, Ipswich and Lowestoft

Surrey

- Surrey History Centre
  www.surreycc.gov.uk/surreyhistoryservice
  Includes various on-line catalogues and indexes

- Croydon Council: Archives
  www.croydon.gov.uk/leisure/artsentertainmentculture/ culture/archives/
- Royal Kingston: Archives and Local History Service
  www.kingston.gov.uk/browse/leisure/museums/ local_history_and_archives.htm
- Lambeth Archives
  www.lambeth.gov.uk/Services/LeisureCulture/Libraries/ Archives.htm
- London Borough of Merton Local Studies Centre
  www.merton.gov.uk/libraries/localstudies.asp
- London Borough of Richmond upon Thames: Local Studies Collection
  www.richmond.gov.uk/home/leisure_and_culture/ local_history_and_heritage/local_studies_collection.htm
- Southwark Local History Library
  www.southwark.gov.uk/DiscoverSouthwark/ LocalHistoryLibrary/
- The London Borough of Sutton: Archives & Local Studies
  www.sutton.gov.uk/
  Search 'archives' and click 'Archives and Local Studies'
- Wandsworth Local History Service
  www.wandsworth.gov.uk/Home/LeisureandTourism/Museum/ mushistory.htm

Sussex

- East Sussex County Council: Local and Family History
  www.eastsussexcc.gov.uk/leisureandtourism/ localandfamilyhistory/
  Includes pages on 'East Sussex Record Office', and 'Local studies resources in libraries'.

- West Sussex County Council: Local Studies
  www.westsussex.gov.uk/ccm/navigation/libraries-and-archives/ libraries/other-library-services/local-studies
- West Sussex County Council: Record Office
  www.westsussex.gov.uk/ccm/navigation/libraries-and-archives/ record-office/

Warwickshire

- Warwickshire County Record Office
  www.warwickshire.gov.uk/countyrecordoffice
  Includes list of parish registers, 19th c. prisoners database, tithe apportionment database, *etc.*
- Birmingham City Archives
  www.birmingham.gov.uk/archives.bcc
- Coventry City Council Local Studies Library
  www.coventry.gov.uk/
  Search 'Local studies library'.
- Coventry Archives
  www.theherbert.org/collections/archives/index.htm
- Shakespeare Birthplace Trust
  www.shakespeare.org.uk/
  Click 'Library and Archives' for various databases relating to Stratford upon Avon sources

Westmorland *see* Cumberland

Wiltshire

- Wiltshire & Swindon Record Office
  www.wiltshire.gov.uk/leisure-and-culture/
       access-to-records/wiltshire-and-swindon-record-office.htm

Worcestershire

- Worcestershire County Council: Record Office
  worcestershire.whub.org.uk/home/wccindex/wcc-records.htm
  Includes page on the History Centre
- Dudley Archives and Local History
  www.dudley.gov.uk/leisure-and-culture/local-history-heritage/
       archive-and-local-history

Yorkshire

- Borthwick Institute of Historical Research
  www.york.ac.uk/inst/bihr/
  Houses York Diocesan archives
- East Riding of Yorkshire Archive and Local Studies Service
  www.eastriding.gov.uk/libraries/archives/archives.html

- East Yorkshire Bibliography
  library.hull.ac.uk
  Union catalogue of several local studies collections in the Hull area, covering the East Riding. Click 'other options: East Yorkshire Bibliography'.
- North Yorkshire County Council: Archive Services
  www.northyorks.gov.uk/
  Search 'Archive'.
- West Yorkshire Archive Service
  www.archives.wyjs.org.uk/
  Covers archives at Bradford, Calderdale, Kirklees, Leeds, Wakefield, and the Yorkshire Archaeological Society, together with information on the West Riding Registry of Deeds.
- Yorkshire Family History Research Centre
  www.yorkshireancestors.com
  Commercial residential centre for family history researchers
- Barnsley Archives and Local Studies Department
  www.barnsley.gov.uk/bguk/Leisure__Culture/Libraries/
       Archives%20and%20Local%20Studies
- Bradford Libraries Archives and Information Service
  www.bradford.gov.uk/information__and__communication/
       library__and__information__services/
  Includes pages on 'Archives and Collections' and 'Local Studies and Family History Sources'
- Doncaster Archives
  www.doncaster.gov.uk/Leisure__in__Doncaster/Libraris/
       Archives__Local__Studies/Doncaster__Archives.asp
- Hull City Archives
  www.hullcc.gov.uk/
  Search 'Archives'.
- Hull City Council: Local Studies Library
  www.hullcc.gov.uk
  Search 'Local studies' and scroll down to title.
- Leeds Local and Family History Research Services
  www.leeds.gov.uk/
  Search 'Local Studies' and click 'Local history'. Includes notes on 'Leeds local indexes'

- Leeds Local Indexes
  www.leedslocalindex.net
  Index to newscuttings, parish registers, the census, etc., at Leeds Public Library
- Rotherham Metropolitan Borough Archives and Local Studies Service
  www.rotherham.gov.uk/graphics/Learning/Archives
- Sheffield Archives
  www.sheffield.gov.uk/in-your-area/libraries/find/archives/ sheffield-archives
- Sheffield City Council Local Studies Library
  www.sheffield.gov.uk/in__your__area/libraries/find/ all__libraries/local-studies-library
- York City Archives
  www.york.gov.uk/leisure/Libraries/York__city__archive/
- York Minster Library
  www.york.ac.uk/services/tmm2003/ York%20Minster%20Library.htm
  Includes on-line book catalogue, and information on the 'Yorkshire Family and Local History Database'

CHANNEL ISLANDS
- Priaulx Library
  www.priaulxlibrary.co.uk
  Includes notes on 'Greffe records' and various other sources
- Société Jersiaise
  www.societe-jersiaise.org/
  Includes pages on the Society's library
- Jersey Heritage Trust
  www.jerseyheritagetrust.org

ISLE OF MAN
- Manx National Heritage: National Library & Archives
  www.gov.im/mnh/heritage/library/nationallibrary.xml

WALES
- Welsh Record Offices and Archives on the Web
  www.oz.net/~markhow/welshros.htm

- Cyngor Archifau a Chofnodion Cymru: Archives and Records Council Wales
  www.llgc.org.uk/cac/
  Includes pages for most Welsh record offices, some of which are also listed separately below
- National Library of Wales
  www.llgc.org.uk
  Extensive; click 'Family History' for a guide to 'Genealogical Sources at the National Library of Wales'.
- Archives Network Wales
  www.archivesnetworkwales.info
  Welsh equivalent of A2A

Anglesey
- Serving Anglesey: Local Studies
  www.ynysmon.gov.uk/doc.asp?cat=1604
  Gives access to pages on Anglesey Archives

Breconshire *see* Montgomeryshire

Caernarvonshire
- Cyngor Gwynedd Council: Archives
  www.gwynedd.gov.uk
  Go to 'Quick Links' and click 'Archives'
- Conwy: Archives
  www.conwy.gov.uk/
  Search 'Archive' and click 'Welcome to the Archives'. Also see 'Local History @ Your Library'

Cardiganshire
- Ceredigion Archives
  www.archifdy-ceredigion.org.uk/

Carmarthenshire
- Carmarthenshire: Archive Service
  www.carmarthenshire.gov.uk/eng/index.asp?docID=6397

Denbighshire
- Denbighshire Record Office
  www.denbighshire.gov.uk/
  Click 'A-Z' and title
  See also **www.genuki.org.uk/big/wal/DEN/DenbighRO/ index.html**

- A. N. Palmer Centre for Local Studies & Archives
  www.wrexham.gov.uk/english/heritage/archives/index.htm
  In Wrexham

Flintshire
- Flintshire: Archives
  www.flintshire.gov.uk/webcont/NewRealweb.nsf/
  vwa__docref/DEVS5RVL98

Glamorganshire
- Glamorgan Record Office
  www.glamro.gov.uk
- West Glamorgan Archive Service
  www.swansea.gov.uk/westglamorganarchives/
  Includes guide to Neath Antiquarian Society and Royal Institution
  of South Wales collections

Merionethshire *see* Caernarvonshire

Monmouthshire
- Gwent Record Office
  www.llgc.org.uk/cac/cac0004.htm/

Montgomeryshire
- Powys County Archives Office
  www.powys.gov.uk/index.php?id=647
  Includes many leaflets, including full listing of Montgomeryshire
  Quarter Sessions records

Pembrokeshire
- Pembrokeshire Record Office
  www.llgc.org.uk/cac/cac0002.html
  www.pembrokeshire.gov.uk
  Search 'Record Office'

Radnorshire *see* Montgomeryshire

4. Family History Societies

Family history societies are invaluable sources of help and information for family historians. You should join one! Read:
- Should I join a Family History Society
  www.ffhs.org.uk/tips/societies.php

Most family history societies have web sites. These generally provide information on the society - names of officers, meetings, membership information, publications, services offered, lists of members interests, links to other web pages, *etc.* Some do much more than this, and particular features are noted below. A full listing of family history societies is given in:
- Family History and Genealogy Societies
  www.genuki.org.uk/Societies/

See also:
- Federation of Family History Societies
  www.ffhs.org.uk/Members2/contacting.php
  List of member societies. This includes some without a web presence.
- Local and Family History Societies in Great Britain
  www.mytimemachine.co.uk/historygroups.htm

National Organisations
- Federation of Family History Societies
  www.ffhs.org.uk
- Guild of One-Name Studies
  www.one-name.org
- Institute of Heraldic and Genealogical Studies
  www.ihgs.ac.uk
- Society of Genealogists
  www.sog.org.uk

Specialist and Overseas Groups
- Anglo-Austrian Family History Group
  www.aafhg.org.uk

- Anglo-French Family History Society
  members.geneaguide.com/affhs/AS-AFFHS.HTM
- Anglo-German Family History Society
  www.feefhs.org.uk/frgagfhs.html
- Anglo-Italian Family History Society
  www.anglo-italianfhs.org.uk/
- British Isles Family History Society-U.S.A.
  www.rootsweb.com/~bifhsusa
- British Isles Family History Society of Greater Ottowa
  www.bifhsgo.ca
- British Records Association
  www.britishrecordsassociation.org.uk/
- Catholic Family History Society
  www.catholic-history.org.uk/cfhs/
- The Families in British India Society
  www.fibis.org
- Family & Community Historical Research Society
  www.fachrs.com
- Family and Local History Indexing Group
  www.flhig.org.uk
  Includes pages on indexing periodicals, the census, and parish registers
- Friends of the National Archives
  www.nationalarchives.gov.uk/friends/
- The Heraldry Society
  www.theheraldrysociety.com
- Jewish Genealogical Society of Great Britain
  www.jgsgb.org.uk
- Quaker Family History Society
  www.qfhs.org.uk
- Railway Ancestors Family History Society
  www.railwayancestors.org.uk
- Romany & Traveller Family History Society
  www.rtfhs.org.uk

County & Local Societies

Bedfordshire
- Bedfordshire Family History Society
  www.bfhs.org.uk

Berkshire
- Berkshire Family History Society
  www.berksfhs.org.uk

Buckinghamshire
- Buckinghamshire Family History Society
  www.bucksfhs.org.uk
- Buckinghamshire Genealogical Society
  www.bucksgs.org.uk/
  Includes parish records listing

Cambridgeshire
- Cambridgeshire Family History Society
  www.cfhs.org.uk
- Cambridge University Heraldic & Genealogical Society
  www.cam.ac.uk/societies/cuhags
- Fenland Family History Society
  www.fenlandfhs.org.uk
  Covers the Isle of Ely, South Lincolnshire and West Norfolk

Cheshire
- Family History Society of Cheshire
  www.fhsc.org.uk
- North Cheshire Family History Society
  www.dramsden.co.uk/ncfhs/

Cornwall
- Cornwall Family History Society
  www.cornwallfhs.com
- Fal Worldwide Family History Group
  beehive.thisiscornwall.co.uk/
  default.asp?WCI=SiteHome&ID=2035
- London Cornish Association: Family History
  www.londoncornish.co.uk/familyhistory.html
- Pacific Northwest Cornish Society
  nwcornishsociety.org/

Cumberland & Westmorland
- Cumbria Family History Society
  cumbriafhs.com

Derbyshire
- Derbyshire Family History Society
  www.dfhs.org.uk
- Chesterfield & District Family History Society
  www.cadfhs.org.uk

Devon
- Devon Family History Society
  www.devonfhs.org.uk

Dorset *see also* Somerset
- Dorset Family History Society
  www.dorsetfhs.org.uk/

Durham *see also* Northumberland
- Cleveland Family History Society
  www.clevelandfhs.org.uk

Essex
- Essex Society for Family History
  www.esfh.org.uk
- Thameside Family History Group
  www.tfhg.org.uk/
  Covers the Grays, Essex area

Gloucestershire & Bristol
- Bristol & Avon Family History Society
  www.bafhs.org.uk
- Gloucestershire Family History Society
  www.gfhs.org.uk

Hampshire
- Hampshire Genealogical Society
  www.hgs-online.org.uk
- Isle of Wight Family History Society
  www.isle-of-wight-fhs.co.uk

Herefordshire
- Herefordshire Family History Society
  www.rootsweb.com/~ukhfhs

Hertfordshire
- Hertfordshire Family History Society
  www.hertsfhs.org.uk/
- Royston and District Family History Society
  www.roystonfhs.org.uk/

Huntingdonshire
- Huntingdonshire Family History Society
  www.huntsfhs.org.uk/

Kent
- Folkestone & District Family History Society
  www.folkfhs.org.uk
- Kent Family History Society
  www.kfhs.org.uk
- Tunbridge Wells Family History Society
  www.tunwells-fhs.co.uk
- North West Kent Family History Society
  www.nwkfhs.org.uk
  Includes parish gazetteer

Lancashire
- Lancashire Family History & Heraldry Society
  www.lfhhs.org.uk/
- Lancashire Parish Register Society
  www.genuki.org.uk/big/eng/LAN/lprs/
- Furness Family History Society
  www.furnessfhs.co.uk
- Lancaster Family History Group
  www.lfgh.org/
- Liverpool & S.W. Lancashire Family History Society
  www.liverpool-genealogy.org.uk/
- Manchester and Lancashire Family History Society
  www.mlfhs.org.uk
- North Meols (Southport) Family History Society
  www.nmfhssouthport.co.uk/
- Ormskirk & District Family History Society
  www.odfhs.org.uk
- St. Helen's Townships Family History Society
  www.sthelenstownshipsfhs.org.uk

Leicestershire
- Leicester & Rutland Family History Society
  www.lrfhs.org.uk

Lincolnshire *see also* Cambridgeshire
- Lincolnshire Family History Society
  www.lincolnshirefhs.org.uk
- Isle of Axholme Family History Society
  www.axholme-fhs.org.uk

London & Middlesex
- London Family History Societies
  homepages.gold.ac.uk/genuki/LND/fhs.html
  Map showing coverage
- Alphabetical List of Parishes
  homepages.rootsweb.com/~bpefisk/fh/FHSs.html
  List of parishes in the greater London area showing the relevant family history society
- East of London Family History Society
  eolfhs.org.uk
- Hillingdon Family History Society
  www.rootsweb.com/~enghfhs/
- London Westminster & Middlesex Family History Society
  www.lnmfhs.dircon.co.uk
- West Middlesex Family History Society
  www.west-middlesex-fhs.org.uk/
- Society of Australian Genealogists London & Home Counties Internet Group
  www.sag.org.au
  Click 'Courses' and 'Special Interest Groups'

Norfolk *see also* Cambridgeshire
- Norfolk Family History Society
  www.norfolkfhs.org.uk/
- Mid-Norfolk Family History Society
  www.mnfhs.freeuk.com/
  www.tsites.co.uk/sites/mnfhs/

Northamptonshire
- Northamptonshire Family History Society
  www.fugazi.demon.co.uk
- Peterborough & District Family History Society
  www.peterborofhs.org.uk/

Northumberland
- Northumberland & Durham Family History Society
  www.ndfhs.org.uk

Nottinghamshire
- Nottinghamshire Family History Society
  www.nottsfhs.org.uk

Oxfordshire
- Oxfordshire Family History Society
  www.ofhs.org.uk/

Rutland *see* Leicestershire

Shropshire
- Shropshire Family History Society
  www.sfhs.org.uk

Somerset
- Somerset & Dorset Family History Society
  www.sdfhs.org/
- Weston Super Mare Family History Society
  www.wsmfhs.org.uk/

Staffordshire *see also* Worcestershire
- Audley and District Family History Society
  www.acumenbooks.co.uk/audleynet/famhist/index.htm
- Burntwood Family History Group
  www.geocities.com/bfhg1986/
- Tipton and Wednesbury Family History Society
  www.genuki.org.uk/big/eng/STS/TWFHS.html
- Walsall Family History Group
  www.wfhg.co.uk
  website.lineone.net/~djwperkins/

Suffolk
- Suffolk Family History Society
  www.suffolk.fhs.co.uk
- Felixstowe Family History Society
  www.itgen.co.uk/ffhs/
- Haverhill Family History Group
  www.haverhill-uk.com/genealogy-home-134.htm.

Surrey
- East Surrey Family History Society
  www.eastsurreyfhs.org.uk
- West Surrey Family History Society
  www.wsfhs.org
- Epsom Family History Group
  members.aol.com/EFHGinfo/
- Reigate & District Family History Group
  www.surreycc.gov.uk/
  Search under name of the Group

Sussex
- Sussex Family History Group
  www.sfhg.org.uk
- Family Roots: the Family History Society for Eastbourne & District
  www.eastbournefhs.org.uk
- Hastings & Rother Family History Society
  www.hrfhs.org.uk

Warwickshire *see also* Worcestershire
- Warwickshire Family History Society
  www.wfhs.org.uk
- Coventry Family History Society
  www.covfhs.org
- Nuneaton and North Warwickshire Family History Society
  www.nnwfhs.org.uk
- Rugby Family History Group
  www.rugbyfhg.co.uk

Westmorland *see* Cumberland

Wiltshire
- Wiltshire Family History Society
  www.wiltshirefhs.co.uk/home.htm

Worcestershire
- Birmingham & Midland Society for Genealogy & Heraldry
  www.bmsgh.org/
  Covers Worcestershire, Warwickshire and Staffordshire.
- Malvern Family History Group
  www.communigate.co.uk/worcs/malvernfamilyhistorygroup/

Yorkshire *see also* Durham (for Cleveland)
- London Group of Yorkshire Family History Societies
  www.genuki.org.uk/big/eng/YKS/Misc/FHS/
- Barnsley Family History Society
  www.barnsleyfhs.co.uk
- Bradford Family History Society
  www.bradfordfhs.org.uk/
- Calderdale Family History Society (incorporating Halifax & District)
  www.cfhsweb.co.uk/
- Doncaster & District Family History Society
  www.doncasterfhs.co.uk/
- East Yorkshire Family History Society
  www.eyfhs.org.uk
- Harrogate and District Family History Society
  www.hadfhs.co.uk
- Huddersfield & District Family History Society
  www.hdfhs.org.uk
- Keighley & District Family History Society
  www.keighleyfamilyhistory.org.uk
- Morley Family History Group
  wakefieldfhs.org.uk/morleyfhg/
- Pontefract & District Family History Society
  www.pontefractfhs.org.uk
- Ripon Historical Society and Family History Group
  www.riponhistoricalsociety.org.uk
- Rotherham Family History Society
  www.rotherhamfhs.co.uk

- Sheffield & District Family History Society
  www.sheffieldfhs.org.uk
- Wakefield Family History Society
  www.wdfhs.co.uk
- Wharfedale Family History Group
  www.wharfedalefhg.org.uk
- Yorkshire Archaeological Society. Family History Section
  www.yorkshireroots.org.uk/core.htm
- City of York & District Family History Society
  www.yorkfamilyhistory.org.uk

CHANNEL ISLANDS
- Family History Section of La Société Guernesiaise
  www.societe.org.gg/sections/familyhistorysec.htm
- Channel Islands Family History Society
  www.channelislands.history.com/

ISLE OF MAN
- Isle of Man Family History Society
  www.isle-of-man.com/interests/genealogy/fhs/
- North American Manx Association
  www.isle-of-man.com/interests/genealogy/nama/

WALES
- Association of Family History Societies of Wales
  www.rootsweb.com/~wlsafhs/index.htm
- Family History and Genealogy Societies - Wales
  www.genuki.org.uk:8080/Societies/Wales.htm
- New Zealand Society of Genealogists: NZSG - Welsh Interest Group
  www.genealogy.org.nz/sig/welsh.html

Anglesey *see* Caernarvonshire

Breconshire
- Powys Family History Society
  www.rootsweb.com/~wlspfhs
  Covers Breconshire, Montgomeryshire, and Radnorshire
- Ystradgynlais Family History Society
  www.ystradgynlaisfhs.co.uk
  On the borders of Glamorganshire and Breconshire

Caernarvonshire
- Gwynedd Family History Society
  www.gwyneddfhs.org.uk
  Covers Anglesey, Caernarvonshire and Merionethshire

Cardiganshire *see also* Carmarthenshire
- Cardiganshire Family History Society
  www.cgnfhs.org.uk

Carmarthenshire
- Carmarthenshire Family History Society
  www.rootsweb.com/~wlscfhs/
- Dyfed Family History Society
  www.dyfedfhs.org.uk
  Covers Cardiganshire, Carmarthenshire and Pembrokeshire

Denbighshire
- Clwyd Family History Society
  clwydfhs.org.uk
  Covers Denbighshire, Flintshire, and part of Merionethshire

Flintshire *see* Denbighshire

Glamorganshire *see also* Breconshire
- Glamorgan Family History Society
  www.rootsweb.com/~wlsglfhs/

Merionethshire *see* Caernarvonshire and Denbighshire

Monmouthshire
- Gwent Family History Society
  www.rootsweb.com/≈wlsgfhs/index.htm

Montgomeryshire *see also* Breconshire
- Montgomeryshire Genealogical Society
  home.freeuk.net/montgensoc

Pembrokeshire *see also* Cardiganshire

Radnorshire *see also* Breconshire

5. Discussion Groups: Mailing Lists, Newsgroups and Message Boards

Want to ask someone who knows? Then join a mailing list or newsgroup. For general information on mailing lists, visit:

- FAQ: Mailing Lists. What are they?
  helpdesk.rootsweb.com/help/mail1.html
- Genealogy Mailing Lists
  homepages.nildram.co.uk/~jimella/mail.htm
  Brief introduction for beginners

When you join a mailing list, you can send and receive messages from every other member of the group. By way of contrast, you do not have to join the Usenet newsgroups in order to use them, but you do need newsreading software. However, some newsgroups are 'gatewayed' to, and can be used as, mailing lists. The most important newsgroup for English genealogists is:

- soc.genealogy.britain

Other relevant newsgroups are:
- alt.genealogy
- soc.genealogy.computing
- soc.genealogy.marketplace
- soc.genealogy.medieval
- soc.genealogy.methods
- soc.genealogy.misc
- soc.genealogy.surnames
- soc.genealogy.surnames.britain
- soc.genealogy.surnames.global

Mailing list gateways to some of these are listed below. An index to their contents is available at:
- Google Groups
  groups.google.com

The authoritative guide to mailing lists is:
- Genealogy Resources on the Internet: Mailing Lists
  www.rootsweb.com/~jfuller/gen_mail.html
  This is international in scope. The UK page includes more information on most of the lists mentioned here, and should be consulted for the most recent information - especially for those lists which do not have their own web page.

See also:
- Genealogy Mailing Lists (Genuki)
  www.genuki.org.uk/indexes/MailingLists.html
- Cyndis List: Mailing Lists
  www.cyndislist.com/mailing.htm

A number of websites offer you the opportunity to post messages/queries on the site itself. Some of these sites will also email the messages to subscribers. For a listing of these sites, see:
- Queries & Message Boards
  www.CyndisList.com/queries.htm

Many mailing lists are hosted by Rootsweb. These are listed at:
- Mailing Lists
  lists.rootsweb.com
  Click 'browse mailing lists' for a complete list of lists, or search the archives

Other important mailing lists are hosted at:
- British-Genealogy.com Forums
  www.british-genealogy.com/forums
- The England Genweb Project Website: Mailing Lists for England
  www.rootsweb.com/~engwgw/engmail.html

- Message Boards United Kingdom and Ireland
  boards.ancestry.com/localities.britisles

- MSN Groups
  groups.msn.com
  Search 'genealogy' to identify numerous groups.
- Roots Chat
  www.rootschat.co.uk
- Yahoo Groups
  groups.yahoo.com
  Click 'Family & Home', and 'Genealogy'.

Some resources are only accessible by email. For these, see:
- Genealogy Resources on the Internet: Email Sites
  www.rootsweb.com/~jfuller/gen_email.html

GENERAL UK MAILING LISTS & MESSAGE BOARDS

The original - and still the largest - genealogical mailing list (international in scope) is:
- Roots-L
  www.rootsweb.com/roots-l/

There are many others:
- ALT-GENEALOGY Mailing list
  groups.google.com/group/alt.genealogy/about
  Gatewayed with alt.genealogy newsgroup
- BRIT-SURNAMES Mailing List
  lists.rootsweb.com/index/intl/UK/BRIT-SURNAMES.html
- BRITISH-CONNECTIONS Mailing List
  lists.rootsweb.com/index/intl/UK/
                          BRITISH-CONNECTIONS.html
- Curious Fox
  www.curiousfox.com
  Contact message board
- England Genealogy
  groups.yahoo.com/groups/ENGLANDGENEALOGY/
- England Genealogy Forum
  www.genforum.genealogy.com/englandcountry/
- ENG-GEN-RESOURCES Mailing List
  lists.rootsweb.com/index/intl/ENG/
                          ENG-GEN-RESOURCES.html

- ENG-ONENAME STUDIES Mailing List
  lists.rootsweb.com/index/intl/ENG/
                          ENG-ONENAMESTUDIES.html
- ENGLAND-GenWeb Mailing List
  lists.rootsweb.com/index/intl/ENG/ENGLAND-GenWeb.html
  lists.rootsweb.com/index/other/WorldGenWeb/
                          ENGLAND-GenWeb.html
  Focuses on the GenWeb project
- ENGLAND-ROOTS Mailing List
  www.rootsweb.com/index/intl/ENG/ENGLAND-ROOTS.html
- englishgeneology
  groups.yahoo.com/group/englishgeneology
- English Genealogy
  groups.msn.com/EnglishGenealogy
- English UK only
  groups.yahoo.com/group/englishukonly/
- English_genealogy
  groups.yahoo.com/group/English_genealogy/
- Family History General
  www.british-genealogy.com/forums/forumdisplay.php?f=345
- Genealogy Beginners
  www.british-genealogy.com/forums/forumdisplay.php?f=40
- GENBRIT Mailing List
  lists.rootsweb.com/index/intl/UK/GENBRIT.html
  Gatewayed with soc.genealogy.britain.
- genealoguk
  groups.yahoo.com/group/genealoguk
  Unlike most groups, encourages advertising - especially of genealogical books, which could answer a large percentage of mailing list queries. Moderated by the author of this directory
- General English Family History
  www.british-genealogy.com/forums/forumdisplay.php?f=21
- UK Genealogical Researchers
  groups.yahoo.com/group/UK_Genealogical_Researchers/
- GEN-TRIVIA-ENG Mailing List
  lists.rootsweb.com/index/intl/ENG/GEN-TRIVIA-ENG.html
  For non-genealogical trivia which may be of interest to genealogists

- GEN-MEDIEVAL Mailing List
  lists.rootsweb.com/index/other/Newsgroup_Gateways/
  GEN-MEDIEVAL.html
  Gatewayed with soc.genealogy.medieval.html
- UK-GENEALOGY-NEWBIES Mailing List
  lists.rootsweb.com/index/intl/UK/
  UK-GENEALOGY-NEWBIES.html
- UK-HISTORY-GROUP Mailing List
  lists.rootsweb.com/index/intl/UK/UK-HISTORY-GROUP.html
- ENG-LOST-CONNECTIONS Mailing List
  lists.rootsweb.com/index/intl/ENG/
  ENG-LOST-CONNECTIONS.html
- United Kingdom Genealogy Forum
  genform.genealogy.com/uk
- Wales Genealogy Forum
  genforum.genealogy.com/wales/

SPECIAL INTERESTS: EMIGRATION
- AUS-CONVICTS Mailing List
  lists.rootsweb.com/index/intl/AUS/AUS-CONVICTS.html
  For convicts transported to Australia
- BRITISH HOME CHILDREN Mailing List
  lists.rootsweb.com/index/intl/CAN/
  BRITISHHOMECHILDREN.html
  Child migrants to Canada, 1800-1930
- Descendants of Home Children
  groups.yahoo.com/group/descendantsofhomechildren/
- Emigration from Britain
  www.british-genealogy.com/forums/forumdisplay.php?f=156
- SOUTH-AFRICA-IMMIGRANTS-BRITISH Mailing List
  lists.rootsweb.com/index/intl/ZAF/
  SOUTH-AFRICA-IMMIGRANTS-BRITISH.html
- SOUTH-AM-EMI Mailing List
  www.rootsweb.com/index/intl/ENG/SOUTH-AM-EMI.html
  Emigrants to South America

SPECIAL INTERESTS: OCCUPATIONS
- Occupations - General Forum
  www.british-genealogy.com/forums/forumdisplay.php?f=162
- Occupations Mailing List
  freespace.virgin.net/anglers.rest/Occupations.htm
- ENG-CANAL-PEOPLE Mailing List
  freespace.virgin.net/anglers.rest/Canalpeople.htm
  lists.rootsweb.com/index/intl/ENG/ENG-CANAL-PEOPLE.html
- Canals and Watermen
  www.british-genealogy.com/forums/forumdisplay.php?f=196
- CHURCHMEN-UK Mailing List
  lists.rootsweb.com/index/intl/UK/CHURCHMEN-UK.html
  For clergy ancestors, *etc.*
- Clergymen
  www.british-genealogy.com/forums/forumdisplay.php?f=39
- UK-COALMINERS Mailing List
  lists.rootsweb.com/index/intl/UK/UK-COALMINERS.html
- Coastguards
  www.british-genealogy.com/forums/forumdisplay.php?f=163
- ENGLAND-FREEDMEN Mailing List
  lists.rootsweb.com/index.intl/ENG/
  ENGLAND-FREEDMEN.html
- British Hatters Mailing List
  lists.rootsweb.com/index/intl/UK/BRITISH-HATTERS.html

- Mercantile Marine Community
  mercantile.ewebs.com
- ENG-PUBS-INNS Mailing List
  lists.rootsweb.com/index/intl/ENG/ENG-PUBS-INNS.html
- Paper Mills & Makers Mailing List
  freespace.virgin.net/anglers.rest/PaperMillsMakers.htm
- Photographers and Old Photographs
  www.british-genealogy.com/forums/forumdisplay.php?f=199
- ENG-TOBACCO-PIPE-MAKERS Mailing List
  lists.rootsweb.com/index/intl/ENG/
  ENG-TOBACCO-PIPE-MAKERS.html
- POSTALWORKERS-UK Mailing List
  lists.rootsweb.com/index/intl/UK/POSTALWORKERS-UK.html
- PRISONS-UK Mailing List
  freespace.virgin.net/anglers.rest/Prisons.htm
- RAILWAY-UK Mailing List
  lists.rootsweb.com/index/intl/UK/RAILWAY-UK.html

- Railwaymen
  www.british-genealogy.com/forums/forumdisplay.php?f=198
- Mariners Mailing List
  lists.rootsweb.com/index/other/Occupations/Mariners.html
- Mariners
  www.british-genealogy.com/forums/forumdisplay.php?f=197
- Boer War Mailing List
  freespace.virgin.net/anglers.rest/BoerWar.htm
- British Regiments
  groups.yahoo.com/britregiments
- UK-79TH REGIMENT Mailing List
  lists.rootsweb.com/index/intl/UK/UK-79TH-REGIMENT.html
- Military: UK Miscellaneous: BOER-WAR Mailing List
  lists.rootsweb.com/index/other/Military:_UK/
  Miscellaneous/BOER-WAR.html
- Crimean War Forum
  www.genforum.genealogy.com/crimeanwar/
- Military: UK Miscellaneous: CRIMEAN-WAR Mailing List
  lists.rootsweb.com/index/other/
  Military:_UK_Miscellaneous/CRIMEAN-WAR.html
- ENG-THAMESWATERMEN Mailing List
  www.rootsweb.com/index/intl/ENG/
  ENG-THAMESWATERMEN.html
- THEATRE-UK Mailing List
  lists.rootsweb.com/index/intl/UK/THEATRE-UK.html
- UK-WATCHMAKERS Mailing List
  lists.rootsweb.com/index/intl/UK/UK-WATCHMAKERS.html

SPECIAL INTERESTS: SOURCES

- UK BMD Main Forum
  www.british-genealogy.com/forums/forumdisplay.php?f=224
- Unwanted Certificates
  www.british-genealogy.com/forums/forumdisplay.php?f=167
- UK-CEMETERIES Mailing List
  lists.rootsweb.com/index/intl/UK/UK-CEMETERIES.html
- British Census
  www.british-genealogy.com/forums/forumdisplay.php?f=30
- Certificates: Births, Marriages and Deaths in the UK
  www.british-genealogy.com/forums/forumdisplay.php?f=41

- Church Registers
  www.british-genealogy.com/forums/forumdisplay.php?f=42
- Free UK Mailing Lists
  lists.rootsweb.com/index/other/FreeUK/
  Various lists for the Free BMD and Free Reg projects, which aim
  to provide databases of civil and parish register indexes.
- Cemeteries: MI-ENGLAND Mailing List
  lists.rootsweb.com/index/other/Cemeteries/MI-ENGLAND.html
- MI-ENGLAND Mailing List
  lists.rootsweb.com/index/intl/ENG/MI-ENGLAND.html
  Devoted to monumental inscriptions
- UK-NEWSPAPER-EXTRACTS Mailing List
  lists.rootsweb.com/index/intl/UK/
  UK-NEWSPAPEREXTRACTS.html
- ENGLISH-OBITS Mailing List
  lists.rootsweb.com/index/intl/ENG/ENGLISH-OBITS.html
- UK 1901 CENSUS
  lists.rootsweb.com/index/intl/UK/UK-1901-CENSUS.html
- Photographers and old photographs
  www.british-genealogy.com/forums/forumdisplay.php?f=199

SPECIAL INTERESTS: MISCELLANEOUS

- Anglo Italian Mailing List
  lists.rootsweb.com/index/other/Ethnic-Italian/
  ANGLO-ITALIAN.html
- BRITISH-JEWRY Mailing List
  lists.rootsweb.com/index/intl/UK/BRITISH-JEWRY.html
- BRITISH NOBILITY Mailing List
  lists.rootsweb.com/index/intl/UK/BRITISH-NOBILITY.html
- Children's Homes-UK-Commonwealth
  groups.msn.com/childrenshomesukcommonwealth
- Copyright & Licence Issues
  www.british-genealogy.com/forums/forumdisplay.php?f=330
- ENG-DESERTED-VILLAGES Mailing List
  lists.rootsweb.com/index/intl/ENG/
  ENG-DESERTED-VILLAGES.html
- ENGLAND-Gen Web
  www.rootsweb.com/index/intl/ENG/ENGLAND-GenWeb.html
  For those with interest in the GenWeb project

- BRITISH PEOPLE 1939-1950 Mailing List
  lists.rootsweb.com/index/intl/UK/
  BRITISHPEOPLE1939-1950.html
- Ethnic Romani: UK - ROMANI mailing list
  lists.rootsweb.com/index/other/Ethnic-Romani/
  UK-ROMANI.html
- Genealogical Computing Mailing Lists
  lists.rootsweb.com/index/other/Genealogical_Computing/
- ENG-GEN-EVENTS Mailing List
  lists.rootsweb.com/index.intl/ENG/ENG-GEN-EVENTS.html
- Heraldry: HERALDRY Mailing List
  lists.rootsweb.com/index/other/heraldry/HERALDRY.html
- Institutions
  www.british-genealogy.com/forums/forumdisplay.php?f=269
- Jewish Roots
  www.british-genealogy.com/forums/forumdisplay.php?f=187
- LEGAL-ENGLISH Mailing List
  lists.rootsweb.com/index/intl/UK/LEGAL-ENGWLS.html
  Legal aspects of genealogical research
- Medieval Forum
  genforum.genealogy.com/medieval/
- UK-NEWCHURCH Mailing List
  lists.rootsweb.com/index/intl/UK/UK-NEWCHURCH.html
  For genealogy relating to members of the New (Swedenborgian) church
- OLD-ENGLISH Mailing List
  lists.rootsweb.com/index/intl/ENG/OLD-ENGLISH.html
  For the discussion of old handwriting and word meanings
- One-Place Study Mailing List
  lists.rootsweb.com/index/other/Miscellaneous/
  ONE-PLACE-STUDY.html
- One Place Studies
  www.british-genealogy.com/forumsdisplay.php?f=177
- Parish Law
  www.british-genealogy.com/forums/forumdisplay.php?f=38
- Reading Old Documents
  www.british-genealogy.com/forums/forumdisplay.php?f=37
- UK-SCHOOLS Mailing List
  lists.rootsweb.com/index/intl/UK/UK-SCHOOLS.html

- ENG-SURNAMES Mailing List
  www.rootsweb.com/index/intl/ENG/ENG-SURNAMES.html
- TRANSCRIPTIONS-UK Mailing List
  lists.rootsweb.com/index/intl/UK/TRANSCRIPTIONS-UK.html
- UK-ROMANI Mailing List
  lists.rootsweb.com/index/intl/UK/UK-ROMANI.html
- ENG-VILLAGES Mailing List
  lists.rootsweb.com/index/intl/ENG/ENG-VILLAGES.html
- UK-WORKHOUSE-HOSPITAL Mailing List
  lists.rootsweb.com/index/intl/UK/
  UK-WORKHOUSE-HOSP.html
  For those with workhouse or hospital connections
- Writing up your family history
  www.british-genealogy.com/forums/forumdisplay.php?f=344

SPECIAL INTERESTS: BOOKS, Cds, *etc.*

- GEN-BOOKS Mailing List
  www.rootsweb.com/index/other/Genealogical_Materials/
  GEN-BOOKS.html
- GEN-MARKET Mailing List
  lists.rootsweb.com/index/other/Newsgroup_Gateways/
  GEN-MARKET.html
  Gatewayed with soc.genealogy.marketplace. For commercial postings
- The GEN-MAT lists
  www2.netdoor.com/~cch/lists/Gen-Mat-Lists.htm
  Mailing lists for genealogical books and services
- GEN-MAT-UKI Mailing List
  lists.rootsweb.com/index/intl/UK/GEN-MAT-UKI.html
- genealogy forum co.uk
  www.genealogyforum.co.uk
  Includes a number of general forums
- ENG-GEN-RESOURCES Mailing List
  lists.rootsweb.com/index/intl/ENG/
  ENG-GEN-RESOURCES.html

REGIONAL, COUNTY, AND LOCAL LISTS

There are numerous lists covering particular areas of England and Wales, far too numerous to list here. The great majority are hosted by the websites listed above, p.27-8. A few are also to be found on family history society pages (see chapter 4).

6. County Pages

A great deal of information is to be found on genealogical county pages. Three organizations have provided pages for every county in England and Wales. Genuki provides the most useful pages, concentrating attention on primary historical information, rather than ongoing and completed research; it has numerous pages on particular parishes. Genweb has some similar information, but also includes query boards for each county, and has more information on current and completed family history research. UKGenealogy offers a wide range of general information on resources. A number of private individuals have also created their own county pages - often including transcripts of original sources - and these are also listed here. A number of sites provide similar information concerning smaller areas; the more important of these are also included below.

Bedfordshire
- Bedfordshire Genuki
  www.genuki.org.uk/big/eng/BDF/
- Bedfordshire Genweb
  www.rootsweb.com/~engbdf
- UKGenealogy: Bedfordshire Research
  www.ukgenealogy.co.uk/bdf.htm

Berkshire
- Berkshire Genuki
  www.brazell.net/genuki/BRK/
- Berkshire, England, Genealogy Resources
  www.rootsweb.com/~engbrk
- UKGenealogy: Berkshire Research
  www.ukgenealogy.co.uk/brk.htm

- Cumnor Parish Record
  www.bodley.ox.ac.uk/external/cumnor/
  Includes transcripts of many sources

Buckinghamshire
- Buckinghamshire Genuki
  met.open.ac.uk/genuki/big/eng/BKM
- Buckinghamshire, England, Genealogy Resources
  www.rootsweb.com/~engbkm
- UKGenealogy: Buckinghamshire Research
  www.ukgenealogy.co.uk/bkm.htm
- The Two Villages Archives Trust
  www.mkheritage.co.uk/tva/index.html
  Milton Keynes and Broughton pages

Cambridgeshire
- Cambridgeshire Genuki
  www.genuki.org.uk/big/eng/CAM
- Cambridgeshire Genealogy
  www.rootsweb.com/~engcam/
- UKGenealogy: Cambridgeshire Research
  www.ukgenealogy.co.uk/cam.htm

Cheshire
- Cheshire Genealogy Webring
  alancheshire.tripod.com/cheshgen.html
- Cheshire Genuki
  www.ukbmd.org.uk.genuki/chs/
- Cheshire Genweb
  www.rootsweb.com/~engchs/
- Alan's Genealogy & Cheshire, England, Page
  alancheshire.tripod.com
- UKGenealogy: Cheshire Research
  www.ukgenealogy.co.uk/chs.htm

Cornwall
- West Country Genealogy
  www.westcountrygenealogy.com/
  Many resources for Cornwall, Devon, Dorset, and Somerset

- Cornwall Genuki
  www.genuki.org.uk/big/eng/Cornwall
- Cornwall Genweb
  www.rootsweb.com/~engcornw/
- Cornwall Online's Genealogy Pages
  www.cornwall-online.co.uk/genealogy.htm
- Cornish Forefathers
  www.cornish-forefathers.com
- UKGenealogy: Cornwall Research
  www.ukgenealogy.co.uk/cornwall.htm
- Cornwall Online Parish Clerks
  cornwall-opc.org/
  Pages for each parish
- Bodmin Moor Local and Family History
  bodmoor.co.uk/
- West Penwith Resources
  west-penwith.org.uk/

Cumberland
- North Pennine Ancestors
  www.northpennineancestors.co.uk/
  Covers Cumberland, Durham, Northumberland and Westmorland
  Primarily interests lists, but also has some general pages
- Cumberland Genuki
  www.genuki.org.uk/big/eng/CUL/
- Cumberland Genweb
  www.rootsweb.com/~engcul
- Cumbria Genweb
  www.rootsweb.com/~engcma/
- Cumbria Genealogy
  www.btinternet.com/~grigg/
  Includes indexes of directories, parish registers, 1851 census, *etc.,etc.*
- Edenlinks: Cumberland and Westmorland Family History and Genealogy
  edenlinks.rootsweb.com
- UKGenealogy: Cumberland Research
  www.ukgenealogy.co.uk/cul.htm

Derbyshire

- Derbyshire Genuki
  www.genuki.org.uk/big/eng/DBY
- County Derbyshire: an England Genweb Project
  www.rootsweb.com/~engdby
- Genealogy and Derbyshire, England
  www.jimella.nildram.co.uk/derbys.htm
- UKGenealogy: Derbyshire Research
  www.ukgenealogy.co.uk/dby.htm
- Yesterdays Journey
  homepages.rootsweb.com/~spire/Yesterday/index.htm
  Indexes to a range of documents from Derbyshire
- Jayne's N.E.Derbyshire
  homepages.rootsweb.com/~spire/index.htm
- North West Derbyshire Sources
  freepages.genealogy.rootsweb.com/~dusk
  Census returns, parish registers, directories, *etc.*
- South Derbyshire Genealogy Pages
  freepages.genealogy.rootsweb.com/~brett/sdindex.htm
  Includes transcripts and indexes of wills, parish registers, trade directories, census, *etc.*
- Welcome to Wirksworth parish records, 1600-1900
  www.wirksworth.org.uk
  Extensive website; includes parish registers 1608-1899, memorial inscriptions, churchwardens accounts 1658-1727, censuses for 1841 and 1881, *etc., etc.* 450,000+ original records from 40 miles around Wirksworth

Devon *see also* Cornwall

- Devon Genuki
  genuki.cs.ncl.ac.uk/DEV/
- Devon Genweb
  www.rootsweb.com/~engdev
- Devon Online Parish Clerks and One-Place Studies
  genuki.cs.ncl.ac.uk/DEV/OPCproject.html
- UKGenealogy: Devon Research
  www.ukgenealogy.co.uk/dev.htm
- Hartland Archives Project
  www.hartlandforum.co.uk/archivesproject/

- Plymouth and Southwest Devon: a genealogical miscellany
  freepages.genealogy.rootsweb.com/~terryw/
  Facsimiles of numerous directories, and many other pages
- South Hams, Devon, England
  homepages.ihug.co.nz/~our4bears/index.html
  Indexes and transcripts of census schedules, parish registers, *etc.*

Dorset *see also* Cornwall

- Dorset Genuki
  www.uk-genealogy.org.uk/genuki/DOR/
- Dorset Online Parish Clerks
  www.dorset-opc.com
- Dorset Genealogy Resources
  www.thedorsetpage.com/Genealogy/
- Dorset Genweb
  www.rootsweb.com/~engdor
- UKGenealogy: Dorset Research
  www.ukgenealogy.co.uk/dor.htm
- Family History @ Poole
  www.pooleview.co.uk/familyhistory/index.htm

Durham *see also* Cumberland

- Durham Genuki
  www.joinermarriageindex.com/pjoiner/genuki/DUR/
- Durham Genealogy
  www.rootsweb.com/~engdur
- UKGenealogy: County Durham
  www.ukgenealogy.co.uk/dur.htm
- Durham Records Online
  www.durhamrecordsonline.com
  Index of census returns, parish registers, and various other records for Easington district, Houghton le Spring, and Stockton, Co. Durham; fee-based

Essex

- Essex Genuki
  www.nivek-systems.co.uk/genuki/ESS
- County of Essex, England, Genweb
  www.rootsweb.com/~engess

- UKGenealogy: Essex Research
  www.ukgenealogy.co.uk/ess.htm
- Records of Earls Colne 1375-1854
  www.colnevalley.com/ecrecords.htm
  Includes virtually all surviving records of the parish, and includes name index

Gloucestershire *see also* Oxfordshire
- Gloucestershire Genuki
  www.genuki.org.uk/big/eng/GLS
- Gloucestershire, England, Genweb
  www.rootsweb.com/~enggls/
- UKGenealogy: Gloucestershire Research
  www.ukgenealogy.co.uk/gls.htm
- The Family History Archive
  hometown.aol.com/k2m3/index.html
  Dedicated to Gloucestershire and Somerset
- Bristol Family History Research Guide
  www.members.lycos.co.uk/acwuk
  Covers parts of Gloucestershire and Somerset as well as Bristol
- The South Cotswold Genealogical and Local History Guide
  www.grahamthomas.com/cotsx.html
  Links page
- Forest of Dean Genealogy Pages
  www.forest-of-dean.net
- Hawkesbury History
  www.hawkesburyhistory.co.uk
  Includes source transcripts and indexes
- Sources for Studying the History of the Village of Randwick, Gloucestershire
  www.randwicksources.org.uk/
  Includes a range of sources

Hampshire
- Hampshire Family History: a directory of Internet sites for Hampshire and Isle of Wight research
  website.lineone.net/~hantshistory/
- Hampshire Genuki
  www.genuki.org.uk/big/eng/HAM/

- Hampshire Genweb
  www.rootsweb.com/~engham
- Hampshire Online Parish Clerk (OPC) Project
  www.knightroots.co.uk
  Click 'Hampshire OPC'
- UKGenealogy: Hampshire Research
  www.ukgenealogy.co.uk/ham.htm
- Isle of Wight, England, Genweb Project
  www.rootsweb.com/~engiow
- UKGenealogy: Isle of Wight Research
  www.ukgenealogy.uk/iow.htm

Herefordshire
- Herefordshire Genuki
  www.genuki.org.uk/big/eng/HEF
- Herefordshire, England, Genweb
  www.rootsweb.com/~enghwr/
- UKGenealogy: Herefordshire Research
  www.ukgenealogy.co.uk/hef.htm

Hertfordshire
- Hertfordshire Genuki
  www.pjoiner.demon.co.uk/genuki/HRT
- County of Hertford, England
  www.rootsweb.com/~enghrt
- UKGenealogy: Hertfordshire Research
  www.ukgenealogy.co.uk/hrt.htm

Huntingdonshire
- Huntingdonshire Genuki
  www.genuki.org.uk/big/eng/HUN
- Huntingdonshire Genealogy: an England Genweb Project Site
  www.rootsweb.com/~enghun
- UKGenealogy: Huntingdonshire Research
  www.ukgenealogy.co.uk/hun.htm

Kent *see also* Sussex
- Kent Genealogy
  users.ox.ac.uk/~malcolm/genuki/big/eng/KEN/

- Kent, England, Genweb
  www.rootsweb.com/~engken
- Kent Online Parish Clerks
  www.kent-opc.org/
- Kent Genealogy
  freepages.genealogy.rootsweb.com/%7Emrawson
- Kent Resources for Genealogists and Family Historians
  www.digiserve.com/peter/
- UKGenealogy: Kent Research
  www.ukgenealogy.co.uk/ken.htm
- West Kent Parish Gazetteer
  www.nwkfhs.org.uk/PARINDEX.HTM
  Includes notes on sources
- Ashford, 1840-1870: a socio-demographic study (study number 2948)
  www.data-archive.ac.uk/findingData/
  snDescription.asp?sn=2948
  Database from the census, parish registers, directories, electoral registers, *etc.*

Lancashire
- Lancashire Genuki
  www.genuki.org.uk/big/eng/LAN/
- Lancashire, England, Genweb
  www.rootsweb.com/~englan
- Online Parish Clerks for the County of Lancashire
  www.lan-opc.org.uk
- UKGenealogy: Lancashire Research
  www.ukgenealogy.co.uk/lan.htm
- Genealogy in Darwen and Blackburn, Lancashire
  ourworld.compuserve.com/homepages/GAFOSTER/
- Historical and Genealogical Information for the Region anciently known as the Salford Hundred now known as Greater Manchester
  www.mancuniensis.info/
- Tameside Local and Family History
  members.aol.com/gayjoliver/Tameside.htm

Leicestershire
- Leicestershire Genuki
  www.genuki.org.uk/big/eng/LEI

- Leicestershire Online Parish Clerks Page
  www.rootsweb.com/~engleiopc/
- Leicestershire: part of the England Genweb Project
  www.rootsweb.com/~englei/
- Leicestershire Roots
  www.leicestershireroots.co.uk
- UKGenealogy: Leicestershire Research
  www.ukgenealogy.co.uk/lei.htm

Lincolnshire
- Lincolnshire Genuki
  www.genuki.org.uk/big/eng/LIN
- Lincolnshire Genealogical Research
  home.wi.rr.com/lincolnshire/
- Lincolnshire Genweb Project
  www.rootsweb.com/~englin
- UKGenealogy: Lincolnshire Research
  www.ukgenealogy.co.uk/lin.htm

London & Middlesex
- Gendocs: Genealogical Research in England and Wales
  www.gendocs.demon.co.uk
  Includes various useful pages of (mainly) London information
- London Genuki
  homepages.gold.ac.uk/genuki/LND/
- London Ancestor
  www.LondonAncestor.com
- Middlesex Genuki
  homepages.gold.ac.uk/genuki/MDX
- Middlesex and Greater London: an England Genweb Project Site
  www.rootsweb.com/~engmdx
- UKGenealogy: Middlesex Research
  www.ukgenealogy.co.uk/mdx.htm

Norfolk
- Norfolk Genuki
  www.origins.org.uk/genuki/NFK/
- Norfolk Genweb Project
  www.rootsweb.com/~engnfk/

- NOAH: Norfolk Online Access to Heritage
  www.noah.norfolk.gov.uk
  norlink.Norfolk.gov.uk
  Index to digitised images of sources
- Norfolk Transcription Archive
  www.genealogy.doun.org/transcriptions/
  Transcripts of parish registers, subsidy returns, muster rolls, *etc.*
  Over 476,000 names
- UKGenealogy: Norfolk Research
  www.ukgenealogy.co.uk/nfk.htm

Northamptonshire
- Northamptonshire Genuki
  www.kellner.eclipse.co.uk/genuki/NTH/
- Northamptonshire Genweb
  www.rootsweb.com/≈engnth
- UKGenealogy: Northamptonshire Research
  www.ukgenealogy.co.uk/nth.htm

Northumberland *see also* Cumberland
- Northumberland Communities
  communities.northumberland.gov.uk
  Pages for each parish, many with facsimiles of original sources, entries from trade directories, *etc.*
- Northumberland Genuki
  www.genuki.bpears.org.uk/NBL/
- Northumberland Genealogy
  www.rootsweb.com/~engnbl/
- UKGenealogy: Northumberland Research
  www.ukgenealogy.co.uk/nbl.htm

Nottinghamshire
- Nottinghamshire Genuki
  www.genuki.org.uk/big/eng/NTT
- Nottinghamshire Genweb
  www.rootsweb.com/~engntt
- UKGenealogy: Nottinghamshire Research
  www.ukgenealogy.co.uk/ntt.htm

Oxfordshire
- The Genealogy of the Cotswolds and Surrounds of England
  www.allthecotswolds.com
  Includes census data, interests lists, *etc.,* for Oxfordshire, Gloucestershire, Wiltshire, Warwickshire, Worcestershire and North Somerset
- Oxfordshire Genuki
  users.ox.ac.uk/~malcolm/genuki/big/eng/OXF
- Oxfordshire, England Genealogy Resources
  www.rootsweb.com/~engoxf/
- UKGenealogy: Oxfordshire Research
  www.ukgenealogy.co.uk/oxf.htm

Rutland
- Rutland Genuki
  www.kellner.eclipse.co.uk/genuki/RUT/
- Rutland Genweb
  www.rootsweb.com/engrut
- UKGenealogy: Rutland Research
  www.ukgenealogy.co.uk/rut.htm

Shropshire
- Shropshire Genuki
  www.genuki.org.uk/big/eng/SAL
- Shropshire Genweb Project
  www.rootsweb.com/~engsal/
- UKGenealogy: Shropshire Research
  www.ukgenealogy.co.uk/sal.htm
- Villages (and townships) on the borders of Shropshire & Staffordshire
  www.geocities.com/fountalnpen/moreton.html
  Includes many transcripts of parish registers, the census, monumental inscriptions, *etc.*

Somerset *see also* Gloucestershire and Oxfordshire
- Somerset Genuki
  www.genuki.org.uk/big/eng/SOM/
- Somerset Genweb
  www.rootsweb.com/~engsom/

Somerset Online Parish Clerks
wsom-opc.org.uk
- UKGenealogy: Somerset Research
www.ukgenealogy.co.uk/som.htm

Staffordshire *see also* Shropshire
- Staffordshire Genuki
www.genuki.org.uk/big/eng/STS
- Staffordshire: Part of the UK Genweb
www.rootsweb.com/~engsts
- UKGenealogy: Staffordshire Research
www.ukgenealogy.co.uk/sts.htm
- Black Country Pages
www.rootsweb.com/~engtwfhs/index.htm
Includes parts of Worcestershire

Suffolk
- Suffolk Genuki
www.genuki.org.uk/big/eng/SFK
- Suffolk Genweb Project
www.rootsweb.com/~engsfk/
- UKGenealogy: Staffordshire Research
www.ukgenealogy.co.uk/sfk.htm

Surrey *see also* Sussex
- Surrey Genuki
homepages.gold.ac.uk/genuki/SRY
- Surrey Genweb Project
www.rootsweb.com/~engsry/
- UKGenealogy: Surrey Research
www.ukgenealogy.co.uk/sry.htm

Sussex
- Sussex Genuki
homepages.gold.ac.uk/genuki/SSX/
- Sussex Genweb Project
www.rootsweb.com/~engssx
- Sussex Online Parish Clerks
www.sussex-opc.org

- UKGenealogy: Sussex Research
www.ukgenealogy.co.uk/ssx.htm
- The Weald of Kent, Surrey & Sussex
thesussexweald.org/

Warwickshire *see also* Oxfordshire
- Warwickshire Genuki
www.genuki.org.uk/big/eng/WAR/
- Pickard's Pink Pages of Warwickshire Genealogy
www.hunimex.com/warwick
Includes various transcripts of sources
- Warwickshire, England
www.geocities.com/Heartland/Park/1784/warwic.html
- Warwickshire Online Parish Clerks
www.hunimex.com/warwick/opc/opc.html
- UK Genealogy: Warwickshire Research
www.ukgenealogy.co.uk/war.htm
- Birmingham: the Workshop of the World
www.bham.de/brum.html

Westmorland *see also* Cumberland
- Westmorland Genuki
www.genuki.org.uk/big/eng/WES/
- Westmorland, England, Genweb
www.rootsweb.com/~engwes
- UKGenealogy: Westmorland Research
www.ukgenealogy.co.uk/wes.htm

Wiltshire *see also* Oxfordshire
- Wiltshire Genuki
www.genuki.org.uk/big/eng/WIL/
- Wiltshire Online Parish Clerks Home Page
homepage.ntlworld.com/david.brown6666/wiltsopc/
- Moonrakers Wiltshire Genealogy
www.moonrakers.org.uk
- Wiltshire: Part of the World Genweb Project
www.rootsweb.com/~engwil
- UKGenealogy: Wiltshire Research
www.ukgenealogy.co.uk/wil.htm

Worcestershire *see also* Oxfordshire and Staffordshire
- Worcestershire Genuki
  www.genuki.org.uk/big/eng/WOR
- UKGenealogy: Worcestershire Research
  www.ukgenealogy.co.uk/wor.htm
- Badsey
  www.badsey.net
  Includes many transcripts of village records

Yorkshire
- Yorkshire Genuki
  www.genuki.org.uk/big/eng/YKS/
- Yorkshire, England, Genweb Project
  www.rootsweb.com/~engyks
- UKGenealogy: Yorkshire Research
  www.ukgenealogy.co.uk/yks.htm

CHANNEL ISLANDS
- Channel Islands Genuki
  genuki.weald.org.uk/CHI
- Alex Glendinning's Channel Islands Pages
  user.itl.net/~glen/Clintro.html
- Channel Islands Genealogy Webring
  www.webring.com/hub?ring=chigenring

Alderney
- Alderney Genuki
  genuki.weald.org.uk/CHI/alex/guernseybailiwickalderney.html
- Channel Islands Genealogy
  www.rootsweb.com/~jfuller/ci.html

Guernsey
- Guernsey Genuki
  genuki.weald.org.uk/CHI/alex/guernsey.html

Jersey
- Al Beagan's Genealogy Notes of Jersey
  users.adelphia.net/~abeagan/jersey.htm
- Jersey Genuki
  genuki.weald.org.uk/CHI/alex/jersey.html

- Jersey Names from the Past
  user.itl.net/~picus/names/index.htm
  Many lists of names - bailiffs, jurats, librarians, harbour master, *etc., etc.*

Sark
- Sark Genuki
  genuki.weald.org.uk/CHI/Alex/guernseybailiwicksark.html

ISLE OF MAN
- Isle of Man Parishes
  www.isle-of-man.com/interests/genealogy/
- Isle of Man Genuki
  www.genuki.org.uk/big/iom/index.html
- Isle of Man: British Isles Genweb Project
  www.britishislesgenweb.org/~iom
- A Manx Note Book
  www.isle-of-man.com/manxnotebook/index.htm
  Includes good bibliography
- Manxroots.com
  www.manxroots.com

WALES
- Wales Genuki
  www.genuki.org.uk/big/wal
- Wales Genweb
  www.walesgenweb.com
- UK Genealogy: Welsh Research
  www.ukgenealogy.co.uk/wales.htm
- Wales History: Family History
  www.bbc.co.uk/wales/history/sites/familyhistory
- Genealogy Wales, Wales/Cymru, the culture, language and history of Wales
  members.tripod.com/~Caryl_Williams/index-2.html
- Gareth's Help Page
  home.clara.net/tirbach/hicks.html
  Mainly relating to Wales
- Wales / Cymru (Cyndi's List)
  www.cyndislist.com/wales.htm

- Discover Wales Genealogy Webring
  www.accessgenealogy.com/rings/w/s/index.htm

Anglesey
- Anglesey Genuki
  www.genuki.org.uk/big/wal/AGY
- Anglesey: Part of the Wales GenWeb Project
  www.rootsweb.com/~wlsagy/index.html
- UK Genealogy: Anglesey
  www.ukgenealogy.co.uk/agy.htm

Breconshire
- Breconshire (Brecknockshire) Genuki
  www.genuki.org.uk/big/wal/BRE/
- Breconshire: Part of the World Gen Web Project
  www.rootsweb.com/~wlsbre/index.html
- UK Genealogy: Breconshire Research
  www.ukgenealogy.co.uk/bre.htm

Caernarvonshire
- Caernarvonshire Genuki
  www.genuki.org.uk/big/wal/CAE/
- Caernarvonshire: Part of the World Gen Web Project
  www.rootsweb.com/~wlscae/index.html
- Caernarfonshire Research
  www.ukgenealogy.co.uk/cae.htm
- Powys Heritage Online
  history.powys.org.uk
  Many pages on local history
- Powys FHS FAQ's + Helpfile
  www.kc3ltd.co.uk/~micronic/faqpfhs.htm

Cardiganshire
- Cardiganshire [Ceredigion] Genuki
  www.genuki.org.uk/big/wal/CGN/
- Cardiganshire: Wales Gen Web
  www.rootsweb.com/~wlscgn/index.html
- UK Genealogy: Cardiganshire Research
  www.ukgenealogy.co.uk/cgn.htm

Carmarthenshire
- Carmarthenshire [Sir Caerfyrddin] Genuki
  www.genuki.org.uk/big/wal/CMN
- Carmarthenshire Genweb
  www.rootsweb.com/~wlscfhs/cmngenweb.htm
- UK Genealogy: Carmarthenshire Research
  www.ukgenealogy.co.uk/cmn.htm

Denbighshire
- Denbighshire Genuki
  www.genuki.org.uk/big/wal/DEN
- Denbighshire Wales Gen Web
  www.walesgenweb.com/~denbighshire/
- UK Genealogy: Denbighshire Research
  www.ukgenealogy.co.uk/den.htm

Flintshire
- Flintshire Genuki
  www.genuki.org.uk/big/wal/FLN/
- Flintshire: Part of the UK Gen Web Project
  www.rootsweb.com/~wlsflnsh/index.html
- UK Genealogy: Flintshire Research
  www.ukgenealogy.co.uk/fln.htm

Glamorganshire
- Glamorgan Genuki
  www.genuki.org.uk/big/wal/GLA
- Glamorgan Wales Genweb
  www.rootsweb.com/wlsgla/
- UK Genealogy: Glamorganshire Research
  www.ukgenealogy.co.uk/gla.htm
- Glamorgan Index
  www.angelfire.com/ga/BobSanders/site.html
- Cardiff Records
  www.btinternet.com/~pat.sewell/cr/cr.html
  Extracts and indexes *etc.* of the book by J. H. Matthews

Merionethshire
- Merionethshire Genuki
  www.genuki.org.uk/big/wal/MER/

- Merionethshire Wales Genweb
  www.rootsweb.com/~wlsmer/
- UK Genealogy: Merionethshire Research
  www.ukgenealogy.co.uk/mer.htm

Monmouthshire
- Monmouthshire Family History
  freepages.genealogy.rootsweb.com/~monfamilies/
                        myfamily-history.htm
  County page, with many transcripts of parish registers and other
  original sources
- Monmouthshire Genuki
  www.genuki.org.uk/big/wal/MON/
- Monmouthshire Genweb Project
  www.rootsweb.com/~wlsmon
- UKGenealogy: Monmouthshire Research
  www.ukgenealogy.co.uk/mon.htm

Montgomeryshire *see also* Breconshire
- Montgomeryshire Genuki
  www.genuki.org.uk/big/wal/MGY/
- Montgomeryshire Wales Genweb Project
  www.rootsweb.com/~wlsmgy
- UK Genealogy: Montgomeryshire Research
  www.ukgenealogy.co.uk/mgy.htm

Pembrokeshire
- Pembrokeshire Genuki
  www.genuki.org.uk/big/wal/PEM/
- Pembrokeshire: a Wales Genweb Project
  www.rootsweb.com/~wlspem/
- UK Genealogy: Pembrokeshire Research
  www.ukgenealogy.co.uk/pem.htm
- Pembrokeshire Roots
  members.lycos.co.uk/Graham_Davies/index.html

Radnorshire *see also* Breconshire
- Radnorshire Genuki
  www.genuki.org.uk/big/wal/RAD/

- Radnorshire Wales Genweb
  www.rootsweb.com/~wlsrad/Radnor.htm
- UK Genealogy: Radnorshire Research
  www.ukgenealogy.co.uk/rad.htm

7. Surnames

The Internet is an invaluable aid for those who want to make contact with others researching the same surname. There are innumerable surname interests lists, family web-sites, and surname mailing lists. The two latter categories will not be listed here; they are far too numerous to be listed in a book of this length.

A wide variety of websites, and all Rootsweb message boards, can be searched by surname at:
- Surname Helper Home Page
  surhelp.rootsweb.com

Those engaged on one-name studies are registered at:
- Register of One-Name Studies
  www.one-name.org/register.shtml

Family web-sites may be identified at the following sites:
- A-Z of Family Surnames from England
  members.tripod.com/~Caryl_Williams/names-7.html
  Unlike the other web-pages listed below, the sites listed here are all English
- Lost Cousins
  www.lostcousins.com
- Personal Home Pages Index
  www.cyndislist.com/personal.htm
  Good starting point, but with American bias
- Surname, Family Associations & Family Newsletters Index
  www.cyndislist.com/surnames.htm
  Lists sites for specific surnames
- Registry of Websites at Rootsweb
  www.rootsweb.com/~websites/
  Scroll down to 'Surname websites'. Probably the most extensive listing of surname sites; American bias

- Surname Resources at Rootsweb
  resources.rootsweb.com/surnames/

There are a number of sites offering surname searches on major databases. These tend to be American biased, but nevertheless have major English content as well. They include:
- Ancestry World Tree
  www.ancestry.com/trees/awt/main.aspx
  Pedigree database containing over 186,000,000+ names
- Ancestry.com: United Kingdom
  www.ancestry.com/search/
  Scroll down and click 'UK & Ireland'. Surname searches on various substantial databases
- Family Relatives
  www.familyrelatives.com
- Gen Circles
  www.gencircles.com
  Pedigree database; pay per view
- Genealogical Gleanings in England
  content.ancestry.com/iexec/?htx=BookList&dbid=28532
  Subscription required. Collection of pedigrees of families who emigrated to North America
- Genealogical Storage and Retrieval Centre
  jrose.dynip.com/gsrc
  For surname searching; also includes list of parish registers
- Genes Reunited
  www.genesreunited.co.uk
  UK pedigree database
- GENi
  www.geni.com
- Genserv
  www.genserv.com/
  Pedigree database; 26,000,000+ names
- My Family
  beta.myfamily.com
- My Heritage
  www.myheritage.com

- The Ogre: online Genealogical Research Engine
  www.cefnpennar.com
  On-line genealogical research engine for UK baptisms, census, burials, directories, marriages and miscellaneous data. Numerous small databases
- One Great Family
  www.onegreatfamily.com
  Subscription based pedigree database
- Surname Navigator
  www.surnamenavigator.org
  Surname searches on a variety of UK databases including the IGI, Ancestral File, Ancestry.com, Debt of Honour register, *etc.* Click 'select country'
- We Relate
  www.werelate.org
- World Connect
  worldconnect.genealogy.rootsweb.com
  Over 480,000,000 names
- World Family Tree
  familytreemaker.genealogy.com/wfttop.html
  Subscription pedigree database; over 183,000,000 names

For surname mailing lists, go to:
- Genealogy Resources on the Internet: Mailing Lists: Surnames
  www.rootsweb.com/~jfuller/gen__mail.html#SURNAMES
- Mailing Lists
  lists.rootsweb.com
  At Rootsweb

Surname Interest Lists
- GENUKI Surname Lists
  www.genuki.org.uk/indexes/SurnamesLists.html
  Leads to 'Online English Names Research Directory' (see below)
- Genealogical Research Directory
  members.ozemail.com.au/~grdxxx/
  Web-page for ordering the book and CD-Rom
- Huguenot Surnames Index
  www.aftc.com.au/Huguenot/Hug.html
  Interest list

- One Name Study Surnames Listings
  www.county-surnames.co.uk/
  list.php?county=One%20Name%20Study
- Online English Names Research Directory
  www.list.jaunay.com/engnames/
  Gateway to surname interests lists for many counties
- Rootsweb Surname List
  rsl.rootsweb.com/
  Probably the largest list of surname interests on the web
- Surnames by Town.com: United Kingdom
  unitedkingdom.surnamesbytown.com
  Interests lists for many towns (listed by county). Includes Gedcom files
- UK Surnames
  www.county-surnames.co.uk
  Surname interest lists for each county

County & Local Lists
In addition to the lists below, many family history societies websites includes lists of their members interests

Bedfordshire
- Bedfordshire Surnames List
  homepages.ihug.co.nz/~hughw/bedf.html
- Bedfordshire Surnames Listings
  www.county__surnames.co.uk/list.php?county=Bedfordshire

Berkshire
- Berkshire Surnames Listings
  www.county-surnames.co.uk/list.php?county=Berkshire

Buckinghamshire
- Buckinghamshire Surnames List
  webpages.charter.net/dcarlsen/genuki/BKM/bucksurname.html
- Buckinghamshire Surnames Listings
  www.county-surnames.co.uk/list.php?county=Buckinghamshire

Cambridgeshire
- Cambridgeshire Surnames Listings
  www.county-surnames.co.uk/list.php?county=Cambridgeshire

Cheshire

- Cheshire Surnames Directory
  cheshirealan.infinology.net/cheshire_surnames/a1.php
- Cheshire Surnames Listings
  www.county-surnames.co.uk/list.php?county=Cheshire

Cornwall

- Cornish Extended Family
  cornish-family.netfirms.com/
  Primarily a surname interest list
- Cornish Surname Index
  ourworld.compuserve.com/homepages/jon_rees/
  CORN_CSI.HTM
- Cornwall Surnames Listings
  www.county-surnames.co.uk/list.php?county=Cornwall

Cumberland

- Cumbria Surnames Listings
  www.county-surnames.co.uk/list.php?county=Cumbria

Derbyshire

- Derbyshire Surnames List
  homepages.ihug.co.nz/~hughw/dby.htm
- Derbyshire Surnames Listings
  www.county-surnames.co.uk/list.php?county=Derbyshire

Devon

- Devon Surnames Listings
  www.county-surnames.co.uk/list.php?county=Devon

Dorset *see also* Somerset

- Dorset Surnames Listings
  www.county-surnames.co.uk/list.php?county=Dorset
- Family History @ Poole
  www.pooleview.co.uk/familyhistory/fhname.htm
  Interests list

Durham *see also* Northumberland

- Durham Surnames Listings
  www.county-surnames.co.uk/list.php?county=Durham

Essex

- Essex Surnames Listings
  www.county-surnames.co.uk/list.php?county=Essex

Gloucestershire

- Gloucestershire Surnames Listings
  www.county-surnames.co.uk/list.php?county=Gloucestershire

Hampshire

- Hampshire/IOW Surname Interest List
  www.np03.dial.pipex.com/surnames/ham/hamname.htm
- Hampshire Surnames Listings
  www.county-surnames.co.uk/list.php?county=Hampshire
- Isle of Wight Surnames Listings
  www.county-surnames.co.uk/
  list.php?county=Isle%20of%20Wight

Herefordshire

- Herefordshire Surnames Listings
  www.county-surnames.co.uk/list.php?county=Herefordshire
- Herefordshire Surname Interests
  www.rootsweb.com/~ukhfhs/surname.html

Hertfordshire

- Hertfordshire Surnames List
  homepages.ihug.co.nz/~hughw/hertford.html
- Hertfordshire Surnames Listings
  www.county-surnames.co.uk/list.php?county=Hertfordshire

Huntingdonshire

- Huntingdonshire Surnames Listings
  www.county-surnames.co.uk/list.php?county=Huntingdonshire

Kent

- Kent Surname Interests List
  www.rootsweb.com/~engken/kentname.htm
- Kent Surnames Listings
  www.county-surnames.co.uk/list.php?county=Kent

Lancashire
- Lancashire Surnames Listings
  www.county-surnames.co.uk/list.php?county=Lancashire
- Genealogical Surname Interests for Lancashire, England
  www.lancslist.com
- Lancashire Surnames
  ourworld-compuserve.com/homepages/GAFOSTER/n-e-lanc.htm
  Covers N.E.Lancashire
- Liverpool Surnames List
  www.liverpool-genealogy.org.uk/Surnames/Surnamesmem.htm
- Manchester Surnames Listings
  www.county-surnames.co.uk/list.php?county=Manchester

Leicestershire
- Leicestershire Surnames Listings
  www.county-surnames.co.uk/list.php?county=Leicestershire

Lincolnshire
- Lincolnshire Surnames
  home.wi.rr.com/lincolnshire/sur1.htm
- Lincolnshire Surnames Listings
  www.county-surnames.co.uk/list.php?county=Lincolnshire

London & Middlesex
- London Surnames Listings
  www.county-surnames.co.uk/list/php?county=London
- Middlesex Surname Interests
  homepages.rootsweb.com/~bpefisk/fh/midsxnms.html
- Middlesex Surnames Listings
  www.county-surnames.co.uk/list.php?county=Middlesex

Norfolk
- Norfolk Surnames List
  ukgeocities.com/davidbooty@btinternet.com/
  NorfolkSurnames/Index.html
- Norfolk Surnames Listings
  www.county-surnames.co.uk/list.php?county=Norfolk

Northamptonshire
- Northamptonshire Surnames List
  www.kellner.eclipse.co.uk/genuki/NTH/Surnames/

- Northamptonshire Surnames Listings
  www.county-surnames.co.uk/list.php?county=Northamptonshire

Northumberland
- Northumberland Surnames Listings
  www.county-surnames.co.uk/list.php?county=Northumberland

Nottinghamshire
- Nottinghamshire Surnames List
  homepages.ihug.co.nz/~hughw/notts.html
- Nottinghamshire Surnames Listings
  www.county-surnames.co.uk/list.php?county=Nottinghamshire

Oxfordshire
- Oxfordshire Surnames Listings
  www.county-surnames.co.uk/list.php?county=Oxfordshire
- OXSIL: Oxfordshire Surname Interest List
  www.rootsweb.com/~oxsil/

Rutland
- Rutland Surnames Listings
  www.county-surnames.co.uk/list.php?county=Rutland

Shropshire
- Shropshire Surnames Listings
  www.county-surnames.co.uk/list.php?county=Shropshire

Somerset
- Somerset & Dorset Surnames Index
  www.bakery.co.uk/sandd/
- Somerset Surnames Listings
  www.county-surnames.co.uk/list.php?county=Somerset

Staffordshire
- Staffordshire Surnames Listings
  www.county-surnames.co.uk/list.php?county=Staffordshire

Suffolk
- The Suffolk Surnames List
  www.suffolk-surnames-list.co.uk

- Suffolk Surnames Listings
  www.county-surnames.co.uk/list.php?county=Suffolk

Surrey
- Surrey Surnames Listings
  www.county-surnames.co.uk/list.php?county=Surrey

Sussex
- Sussex Surnames Listings
  www.county-surnames.co.uk/list.php?county=Sussex

Warwickshire
- Warwickshire Surnames List
  homepages.ihug.co.nz/~hughw/warwick.html
- Warwickshire Surnames Listings
  www.county-surnames.co.uk/list.php?county=Warwickshire

Westmorland *see also* Cumberland

Wiltshire
- Wiltshire Surnames Listings
  www.county-surnames.co.uk/list.php?county=Wiltshire

Worcestershire
- Worcestershire Surnames Listings
  www.county-surnames.co.uk/list.php?county=Worcestershire

Yorkshire
- Yorkshire Surname List
  www.genuki.org.uk/big/eng/YKS/YKSlist/yks.htm
- Yorkshire Surnames Listings
  www.county-surnames.co.uk/list.php?county=Yorkshire
- Knaresborough Family History
  www.knaresborough.co.uk/history/family/

CHANNEL ISLANDS
- Channel Islands Genealogy - Surname Interests List
  www.rootsweb.com/~jfuller/ci/surnames.html
- Channel Isles Surnames Listings
  www.county-surnames.co.uk/list.php?county=Channel%20Isles

ISLE OF MAN
- Isle of Man Surnames Listings
  www.county-surnames.co.uk/
  list.php?county=Isle%20of%20Man

WALES
- Online Welsh Names Directory
  www.list.jaunay.com/wlsnames/
- Welsh Ancestor List
  www.jlb2005.plus.com/wales/listfram.htm
- Wales Surnames Listings
  www.county-surnames.co.uk/list.php?county=Wales

8. Sources

Information on a wide range of sources is available on the net. An increasing number of sites offer collections of databases. These include indexes, transcripts, and an increasing number of digitised images. For a listing of free databases, see:

- Free Databases for Genealogical Searching
  www.ormond.i8.com

For a rather dated listing of sites providing genealogical sources, see:
- Sites with Genealogical Source Material: UK data
  freespace.virgin.net/alan.tupman/sites

The major general collections of databases are:
- Ancestry.co.uk
  www.ancestry.co.uk
  Many databases and indexes of parish registers, directories and other sources. Commercial site.
- British History Online
  www.british-history.ac.uk
  Includes copies of many published sources, as well as many volumes of the *Victoria County History*
- Documents Online
  www.nationalarchives.gov.uk/documentsonline
  Digitised documents from the National Archives; pay per view site
- Find My Past
  www.findmypast.com
  Collection of databases; pay per view
- Family History Online
  www.familyhistoryonline.co.uk
  Includes over 300 large pay per view databases, including indexes to the census, parish registers, (including portions of the *National burials index*), monumental inscriptions, and other miscellaneous sources. Important, but soon to be taken over by Find My Past

- The Original Record.com
  www.the originalrecord.com
  Index to wide range of original sources (many of which are published); 10,000,000 entries. Pay per view
- Roots.uk
  www.rootsuk.com
  Includes census transcripts and civil register. Pay per view
- UK GENEALOGY
  www.uk-genealogy.org.uk
  Includes many transcripts and indexes of original sources, such as parish registers, trade directories, the *Return of owners of land 1873, etc.,* also county pages
- UK Transcriptions Website
  UK-transcriptions.accessgenealogy.com
  Transcriptions of parish registers, inscriptions, lay subsidies, *etc.,* mainly from Northamptonshire, Shropshire, Staffordshire, Warwickshire and Worcestershire
- Midland Historical Data
  www.midlandshistoricaldata.org/index.html
  Collection of pay per view databases; also available on CD
- Local History: Staffordshire Historical Collections
  www.british-history.ac.uk/subject.asp?subject=5&gid=98
  Transcript of many published volumes, including court records, cartularies, tax lists, *etc.*

Many of the sites listed below provide valuable advice on the location and use of records, rather than the records themselves. In general, I have not included the purely local here; such sites can be easily found via the various county sites listed in Chapter 6, especially the Genuki sites. Some are also listed by the other web directories in the present series.

Absent Voters Lists
- Accrington 1918 Absent Voters List
  www.pals.org.uk/avl/
- Absent Voters in Grimsby & Cleethorpes in 1919
  www.angelfire.com/de/delighted/voters.html
- Leeds Absent Voters List 1914-1918 War
  www.leeds.gov.uk
  Search 'absent voters' and click title.

- Absent Voters List for the Constituency of Wakefield
  www.wakefieldfhs.org.uk/abscent%20voters.htm

Alien Registration Cards
- Alien Registration Cards (1876-1991)
  www.nationalarchive.gov.uk/documentsonline/aliens.asp
  Pay per view. Details of c.1000 aliens, mainly in the London area.

Ancient Petitions
- Ancient Petitions, Henry III-James I
  www.nationalarchives.gov.uk/documentsonline/petitons.asp
  Pay per view

Births, Marriages and Deaths *see also* Civil Registration, International Genealogical Index, Marriages, Nonconformist registers *and* Parish Registers

Thousands of sites are listed in the companion volume in this series, *Births Marriages and Deaths on the Web.* 2nd ed. 2 vols. F.F.H.S., 2005. Only a few of the most important can be listed here.
- UK BDM Exchange
  www.ukbdm.co.uk
  Details from certificates and parish registers. Subscription site
- Births, Marriages and Deaths
  www.familyrecords.gov.uk/topics/bmd.htm
- Resources: Births
  www.findmypast.com/resources/births/
  Also pages on **/marriages** and **/deaths**
- Resources: Overseas Records
  www.findmypast.com/resources/overseasrecords/
  Of births, marriages and deaths
- Births, Marriages and Deaths at Sea
  www.nationalarchives.gov.uk/catalogue/ researchguidesindex.asp
  Click title.
- Births, Marriages and Deaths Overseas
  www.history.ac.uk/gh/overseas.htm
  Leaflet from the Guildhall Library

Bookplates
- The Bookplate Society
  www.bookplatesociety.org

Booth's Survey
- Charles Booth Online Archive: Charles Booth and the survey into life and labour in London (1886-1903)
  booth.lse.ac.uk
  Includes names of many interviewees

Brass Rubbings
- Brass Rubbings: an index of the collections in the West Country Studies Library
  www.devon.gov.uk/etched?__IXP__=1&1XR=100301
  National in scope

Business Records
- Sources for Business History
  www.nationalarchives.gov.uk/nra/guides/
  Click title. Listed in the National Register of Archives
- Business Records at Guildhall Library
  www.history.ac.uk/gh/busimnu.htm
  Includes useful bibliography

Cartularies, Charters, *etc.*
- Cartularies
  paleo.anglo-norman.org/cart.html
  Introduction

Buckinghamshire
- Early Buckinghamshire Charters
  www.buckscc.gov.uk/brs__volumes/03.pdf
- The Cartulary of Missenden Abbey
  www.buckscc.gov.uk/brs__volumes/02.pdf
  Digitised images of a Buckinghamshire Record Society volume

Cumberland
- Register & Records of Holme Cultram
  www.british-history.ac.uk/source.asp?pubid=399
  Transcript of a published cartulary

Derbyshire
- Catalogue of Wolley Charters
  www.bl.uk/catalogues/wolleycharters/
  Deeds and charters, medieval-19th c., relating to Derbyshire and neighbouring counties

London & Middlesex

- London: Monastic and Cathedral Records
  www.british-history.ac.uk/place.asp?gid=87&region=1
  Includes records of the Grey Friars (including monuments) and of
  St. Paul's; also chantry certificates 1548, all transcribed from
  London Record Society volumes

Suffolk

- Blythburgh Priory Cartulary
  content.ancestry.com/iexec/?htx=List&dbid=7606
  Subscription required
- Bury St. Edmunds Abbey Archives
  content.ancestry.com/iexec/?htx=List&dbid=7449
  Subscription required
- Cartulary of the Augustinian Friars of Clare
  content.ancestry.com/iexec/?htx=List&dbid=7577
  Subscription required
- Dodnash Priory Charters
  content.ancestry.com/iexec/?htx=List&dbid=7582
  Subscription required
- Eye Priory Cartulary and Charters
  content.ancestry.com/iexec/?htx=List&dbid=7611
  Subscription required
- Leiston Abbey Cartulary and Butley Priory Charters
  content.ancestry.com/iexec/?htx=List&dbid=7571
  Subscription required
- Sibton Abbey Cartularies and Charters
  content.ancestry.com/iexec/?htx=List&dbid=7470
  Subscription required
- Stoke by Clare Cartulary
  content.ancestry.com/iexec/?htx=List&dbid=7617
  Subscription required
- Charters of St. Bartholomew's Priory, Sudbury
  content.ancestry.com/iexec/?htx=List&dbid=7614
  Subscription required

Yorkshire

- Early Yorkshire Families
  content.ancestry.com/iexec/?htx=List&dbid=8549
  Subscription required. Collection of medieval deeds and charters

Catholic Records

- Catholic Recusants
  www.nationalarchives.gov.uk/catalogue/
  researchguidesindex.asp
  Click title
- Catholic Records
  www.familyrecords.gov.uk/frc/pdfs/catholic_records.pdf
- The Recusant Historians Handbook
  www.catholic-history.org.uk/nwchs/recushandbook.htm
- The Catholic Historians Handbook 1829-1965
  www.catholic-history.org.uk/nwch/plumb/contents.html
- Catholic Record Society
  www.catholic-history.org.uk/crs
  Many valuable source publications listed
- Catholic National Library
  www.catholic-library.org.uk
  Includes list of mission register transcripts held (see under
  'special collections')
- Catholic Family History Society: Index to *ECA Journal* and
  Catholic Ancestor
  www.catholic-history.org.uk/cfhs/ancestor.htm
- Thames Valley Recusants
  www.users.globalnet.co.uk/~hadland/rec.html
  Berkshire and Oxfordshire. Various articles
- Catholic History in South West England
  content.ancestry.com/iexec/?htx=List&dbid=7796
  Subscription required. Data from OLIVER, GEORGE. *Collections
  illustrating the history of the Catholic religion in the counties of
  Cornwall, Devon, Dorset, Somerset, Wilts & Gloucester.* Charles
  Dolman, 1857.
- List of Papists and Delinquents Sequestered in North Devon 1648
  genuki.cs.ncl.ac.uk/DEV/DevonMisc/Papists.html
- Persons presented as Popish Recusants in the reigns of James I
  and Charles I
  freespace.virgin.net/guy.etchells/prindex.htm
  In Nottinghamshire
- The Papists of Kendale
  www.edenlinks.co.uk/HISTORY/PAPISTS_ETC.HTM
  List, 1650

Census Records

A number of useful introductions to the study of censuses are available on the web. These include:

- The British Census: Searching the British Census
  globalgenealogy.com/globalgazette/gazrr/gazrr115.htm
- Census of England and Wales: Read this first
  www.nationalarchives.gov.uk/catalogue/
  researchguidesindex.asp
  Click title
- Census Records 1841-1891
  globalgenealogy.com/globalgazette/gazfd/gazfd29.htm
  Introduction. Continued at **/gazfd30.htm**
- Census Records: United Kingdom
  www.cogen.com/CensusRecordsUK
- Census Returns
  www.familyrecords.gov.uk/frc/research/censusmain.htm
  Introduction from the Family Records Centre
- England and Wales: Census
  www.genuki.org.uk/big/eng/census.html
  Genuki page
- England: How to Use Census Records
  www.familysearch.org
  Click 'search', then 'research help', go to 'E' (for England) and scroll down to title

Hundreds of sites provide census information. There are a number of useful links pages and directories:

- British Census Indexes, Transcripts and Images Available Online or on CD
  www.mit.edu/~dfm/genealogy/census-chart.html
  Directory of resources
- Census finder: a directory of free census records
  www.censusfinder.com
- Links to Online Census Records: England
  www.census-online.com/links/England/
- Census links: England
  censuslinks.com/
  Click 'England'
- United Kingdom and Ireland Census
  www.genuki.org.uk/big/Census.html

- UK BMD: Census Sites with Online Data
  www.ukbmd.org.uk/index.php
  Click 'census' for gateway to many census databases
  Other sites providing useful general information include:
- The Census Enumerators Books
  www.staffs.ac.uk/schools/humanities_and_soc_sciences/
  census/cebs.htm
  Introduction aimed at sociologists, which may also be useful for genealogists in understanding census documents.
- Census UK
  www.censusuk.co.uk
  Free look-up service
- The Enumeration of People not in normal households on Census Night
  www.gendocs.demon.co.uk/census2.html
- Census Returns for England and Wales
  www.gendocs.demon.co.uk/census.html
  Lists questions asked by enumerators, 1841-1901
- UK Census Websites
  www.ukcensusonline.co.uk
  Introductory pages on each census except 1881, including details of Cd's and online indexes available from S & N

There are a large number of sites offering indexes, digitised images, and transcripts of census returns. The great majority of these are local and county-wide, and will not be listed here. Those which are national in scope include:

- Ancestry.co.uk
  www.ancestry.co.uk
  Includes indexes and digitised images of census returns 1841-1901. Subscription required.
- British Origins
  www.originsnetwork.com/help/popup-aboutbo.htm
  Digitised images for 1841, 1861 and 1871, with indexes. Pay per view
- Find My Past: Census Records
  www.findmypast.com/
  Click 'Census'. 1841 & 1861-91. Pay per view.

- The Genealogist: the UK Census Online
  www.thegenealogist.co.uk
  Indexes and transcripts of all censuses, 1841 to 1901. Subscription required.
- UK Census Online
  freecen.rootsweb.com
  Major project to provide a free online searchable database of 19th century UK census returns

Some sites provide indexes and digitised images for particular census years:
- 192.com
  www.192.com/Genealogy
  1861 only
- Family Search
  www.familysearch.org
  Index and transcript of the 1881 census. For the '1881 British Census Indexes Resource Guide', click 'Research Helps', 'E' (for England) and scroll down to title
- UK 1881 Census and Index
  www.apex.net.au/~tmj/uk1881cs.htm
  Includes list of corrections to the 1881 census index fiche, and guide to 'Finding an address in the transcription of the 1881 census of England and Wales'
- 1901 Census Online
  www.1901census.nationalarchives.gov.uk
  Index and digitised images. Pay per view site
- The 1901 Census: Institutions
  homepage.ntlworld.com/jeffery.knaggs/Instuts.html
  List of institutions enumerated separately
- 1901 Census: Royal Navy Ships
  homepage.ntlworld.com/jeffery.knaggs/RNShips.html
  Index to ships at sea on census night
- 1901 Leftovers
  1901census.rootschat.com/
  Details from the 1901 census posted by contributors
- 1911 Census
  www.nationarchives.gov.uk/1911census

For overseas people in the censuses, see:
- Entries in UK censuses for people born in the Australian colonies
  www.apex.net.au/~tmj/aus-cns.htm
- Entries in UK censuses for people born in Jamaica
  www.candoo.com/genresources/jam-cns__off.htm

Census, Pre-1841
- Bedfordshire Local Census Listings
  www.genuki.org.uk/big/eng/BDF/LocalCensusListings/index.html
  Unofficial censuses
- Constables Census Westmorland 1787
  www.edenlinks.co.uk/RECORDS/CC/CCINDEX.HTM
- Index to 1849 Map of Jersey
  www.rootsweb.com/~jfuller/ci/1849map/intro.html
  An unofficial 'census' listing householders
- St. Asaph Notitiae
  www.llgc.org.uk/Notitiae/nll__sOO1.htm
  Lists of heads of households for the Diocese of St.Asaph (which covered much of North Wales), 1681. Facsimiles of the original documents

Church Records
- Church Records
  www.medievalgenealogy.org.uk/guide/ecc.shtml
- Index to the Act Book of the Archbishops of Canterbury 1663-1859
  content.ancestry.com/iexec/?BookList&dbid=28558
  Subscription required
- The Church in London 1375-1392
  www.british-history.ac.uk/source.asp?pubid=157
  Includes taxation of the clergy, and ecclesiastical estate records
- London: Religious Organisations, Records of
  www.british-history.ac.uk/place.asp?gid=68&region=1
  Transcripts of several London Record Society volumes relating to various denominations, mainly 18th c.
- London Consistory Court Depositions Index 1700-1713
  www.originsnetwork.com/help/popup-aboutbo-lccd.htm
  Pay per view database
- St. Paul's Cathedral Archives at Guildhall Library
  www.history.ac.uk/gh/stp.htm

- Norfolk Record Office Guide to Holdings: Ecclesiastical Records
  archives.norfolk.gov.uk/guide/nroecc.htm
- The Diocese of Bangor in the Sixteenth Century, being a digest of the registers of the bishops, A.D. 1512-1646
  content.ancestry.com/iexec/?htx=BookList&dbid=29668
  Subscription required

Churchwardens Accounts

- Churchwardens Accounts
  www.york.ac.uk/inst/bihr/guideleaflets/Churchwarden.pdf

Suffolk

- Boxford Churchwardens Accounts 1530-1561
  content.ancestry.co.uk/iexec/?htx=List&dbid=7562
  Subscription required
- Churchwardens Accounts of Cratfield, 1640-1660
  content.ancestry.com/iexec/?htx=List&dbid=7593
  Subscription required

Worcestershire

- Badsey Churchwardens Accounts 1525-1571
  www.badsey.net/past/cwardens.htm

Civil Registration

A new index to the civil registers is currently in preparation. Until that becomes available, the old indexes must still be consulted. Digitised images are available on a number of websites:
- Births, Marriages and Death Certificates: BMD Index
  www.BMDindex.co.uk
  Civil registers index 1837-2003. Subscription required
- England and Wales BMD Index 1837-2005
  www.ancestry.co.uk/search/rectype/vital/freebmd/bmd.aspx
  Free searches of civil registration indexes
- Family Relatives
  www.familyrelatives.org
  Civil registration indexes online. Pay per view site
- Find my past: Births, Marriages and Deaths 1837-2005
  www.findmypast.com/BirthsMarriagesDeaths.jsp
  Civil Registration indexes online. Pay per view.

- Free B.M.D.
  freebmd.rootsweb.com/
  Project to provide free internet access to English and Welsh civil registration records.

A gateway to an increasing number of indexes to the registers of district registrars is provided by:
- UK BMD: Births, Marriages, Deaths and Censuses on the Internet
  www.ukbmd.org.uk

A wide range of sites offering general advice on civil registration records are available:
- Births, Marriages and Deaths in England and Wales since 1837
  www.ancestry.com/learn/library/article.aspx?article=3450
- England: Civil Registration
  www.genuki.org.uk/big/eng/CivilRegistration.html
- A Comedy of Errors: the story of the civil registration of births, marriages and deaths in England and Wales in the 1800s
  homepages.paradise.net.nz/mikefost/
  Details of a critical review of civil registration indexes
- Civil Registration in England and Wales
  www.genuki.org.uk/big/eng/civreg/
- English and Welsh Register Offices
  www.genuki.org.uk/big/eng/RegOffice/
  List
- Barbara's Registration Web Page: England and Wales Birth, Marriage and Death Certificate Information
  home.clara.net/dixons/Certificates/indexbd.htm
  Guide to the information on certificates
- A Comedy of Errors continues ... the Marriage records of England and Wales
  globalgenealogy.com/globalgazette/gazfd/gazfd38.htm
- Registration Districts in England and Wales (1837-1974)
  www.ukbmd.org.uk/genuki/reg/
  Historical information on registration districts
- G.R.O. Indexes Registration Districts
  www.genuki.org.uk/big/eng/civreg/GROIndexes.html
  Details of reference numbers used for districts in the G.R.O. indexes

- General Register Office
  www.gro.gov.uk/
- Ordering Birth Registration Certificates from England and Wales: Using the LDS Family History Center's resources
  www.oz.net/~markhow/ukbirths.htm
- The St.Catherines Marriage Index
  www.cs.ncl.ac.uk/genuki/StCathsTranscriptions
  Includes selective extracts of volumes covering Essex and South Suffolk, 1839-44, and a few other places.
- Birth, Marriage and Death Certificates and other records
  www.familyhistoryonline.net/database/UnrelatedCerts.shtml
  Pay per view database; index to certificates donated to Birmingham & Midland Society for Genealogy & Heraldry
- The UK B.D.M. Exchange
  www.ukbdm.co.uk/
  For exchange of details from certificates

Coroners Inquests
- Coroners Inquests
  www.nationalarchives.gov.uk/catalogue/
  researchguidesindex.asp
  Click title
- Coroners Records
  www.kcl.ac.uk/depsta/law/research/coroners/records.html
- Coroners Records for London and Middlesex
  www.cityoflondon.gov.uk/Corporation/leisure_heritage/
  libraries_archives_museums_galleries/lma/
  visitor_information/free_information_leaflets.htm
  In the City of London Record Office. Click title

Court Records
- Ancestors and the Law
  www.nationalarchives.gov.uk/familyhistory/guide/
  ancestorslaw/default.htm
  Includes many pages on procedures and records in various courts
- England: How to Use Court Records
  www.familysearch.org
  Click 'search', 'research helps', 'E' (for England), and scroll down to title

- Sources for the History of Crime and the Law in England
  www.nationalarchives.gov.uk/catalogue/researchguidesindex.asp
  Click title
- Criminal Courts in England and Wales from 1972
  www.nationalarchives.gov.uk/catalogue/researchguidesindex.asp
  Click title
- The Anglo-American Legal Tradition: Documents from Medieval and Early Modern England from the National Archives in London
  aalt.law.uk.edu
  Digitised images of proceedings in various courts

Assizes
- Assizes: Criminal Trials
  www.nationalarchives.gov.uk/catalogue/researchguidesindex.asp
  Click title
- Assize Records
  www.british-history.ac.uk/catalogue.asp?gid=50
  Transcript of several volumes published by the London Record Society relating to London assizes, 14-16th c.

Chancery
- Chancery Proceedings: Equity Suits after 1558
  www.nationalarchives.gov.uk/catalogue/researchguidesindex.asp
  Click title. There is also a page 'before 1558'.
- Equity Pleadings Database
  www.nationalarchives.gov.uk/equity/
- A Calendar of Chancery Proceedings: bills and answers filed in the reign of King Charles I
  content.ancestry.com/iexec/?htx=BookList&dbid=28535
  Subscription required
- Index of Chancery Proceedings (Reynardson's Division) preserved in the Public Record Office, 1649-1714
  content.ancestry.com/iexec/?htx=BookList&dbid=28549
  Subscription required
- British Chancery Records 1386-1558
  www.ancestry.com/search/db.aspx?dbid=7919
  Subscription required
- Inheritance Dispute Index 1574-1717
  www.originsnetwork.com/help/popup-aboutbo-indis.htm
  Subscription database of 26,000 cases in the Court of Chancery

Exchequer

- Equity Proceedings in the Court of Exchequer
  www.nationalarchives.gov.uk/catalogue/researchguidesindex.asp
  Click title

Eyres

- The General Eyres 1194-1348
  www.nationalarchives.gov.uk/researchguidesindex.asp
  Click title
- The London Eyre of 1244
  www.british-history.ac.uk/sources.asp?pubid=153
  Digitised copy of a London Record Society publication of 1970
- The London Eyre of 1276
  www.british-history.ac.uk/sources.asp?pubid=156
  Digitised copy of a London Record Society publication of 1976

Great Sessions

- Crime and Punishment
  www.llgc.org.uk/sesiwn__fawr/index__s.htm
  Database of the Court of Great Sessions gaol files, 1730-1830

Kings Bench

- Kings Bench (Crown Side) records 1675-1875
  www.nationalarchives.gov.uk/catalogue/researchguidesindex.asp
  Click title

Old Bailey

- Old Bailey and the Central Criminal Court: criminal trials
  www.nationalarchives.gov.uk/researchguidesindex.asp
  Click title
- Old Bailey Proceedings Online
  www.shef.ac.uk/hri/projects/projectpages/oldbailey.htm
- The proceedings of the Old Bailey, London, 1674 to 1834
  www.oldbaileyonline.org/
  Database of 101,102 trials

Requests

- Court of Requests, 1485-1642: a court for the 'poor'
  www.nationalarchives.gov.uk/catalogue/researchguidesindex.asp
  Click title

Star Chamber

- The Court of Star Chamber 1485-1642
  www.nationalarchives.gov.uk/catalogue/researchguidesindex.asp
  Click title

Supreme Court

- Supreme Court, Chancery Division: Cases after 1875
  www.nationalarchives.gov.uk/catalogue/researchguidesindex.asp
  Click title
- Supreme Court: Appeal Cases after 1875
  www.nationalarchives.gov.uk/catalogue/researchguidesindex.asp
  Click title

Wards & Liveries

- Court of Wards and Liveries 1540-1645: Land Inheritances
  www.nationalarchives.gov.uk/catalogue/researchguidesindex.asp
  Click title

Datestones

- Guernsey Datestones
  www.societe-jersiaise.org/alexgle/stonegsy.html
  Index of datestones on houses
- The Jersey Datestones Register
  www.societe-jersiaise.org/alexgle/stonejsy.html

Death Duty Registers

- Resources: Death Duty Registers
  www.findmypast.com/resources/deathdutyregisters/
- Death Duty Registers, 1796-1811
  www.nationalarchives.gov.uk/documentsonline/death-duty.asp
  Digitised images with indexes. Subscription based
- Death Duty Records from 1796
  www.nationalarchives.gov.uk/catalogue/researchguidesindex.asp
  Click title
- How to Interpret Death Duty Registers
  www.nationalarchives.gov.uk/catalogue/researchguidesindex.asp
  Click title

Deeds *see* Title Deeds

Deeds Registries

- The Middlesex Deeds Registry 1709-1938
  www.cityoflondon.gov.uk/Corporation/leisure_heritage/
  libraries_archives_museums_galleries/lma/
  visitor_information/free_information_leaflets.htm
  Click title
- Using The East Riding Register of Deeds
  www.eastriding.gov.uk/libraries/archives/pdf/
  Register_of_Deeds.pdf
- West Yorkshire Archive Service: Registry of Deeds
  www.archives.wyjs.org.uk/
  Click 'Registry of Deeds'

Diaries & Journals

- The Diary Junction
  www.pikle.demon.co.uk/diaryjunction.html
  Information on 500+ diaries
- Two East Anglian Diaries 1641-1729
  content.ancestry.co.uk/iexec/?htx=List&dbid=7624
  Subscription required. Diaries of Isaac Archer and William Coe
- Personal Records: Ralph Josselin's Diary
  linux02.lib.cam.ac.uk/earlscolne/diary/
  Full transcript of an Essex clergyman's diary, 1617-83
- Southwold Diary of James Maggs 1818-1876
  content.ancestry.com/?htx=BookList&dbid=7477
  Subscription required
- Oake's Diaries 1778-1827
  content.ancestry.com/iexec/?htx=List&dbid=7548
  Subscription required. Diary of James Oakes, of Bury St. Edmunds
- John Ostle's Journal
  www.users.tinyworld.co.uk/peterostle/journalx.html
  Extracts, 1855-86 from a Cumbrian farmer's journal
- Roger Whitley's Diary 1648-1697
  www.british-history.ac.uk/source.asp?pubid=121
  Diary of a Cheshire MP

Directories *see* Trade Directories

Divorce Records

- Divorce Records before 1858
  www.nationalarchives.gov.uk/catalogue/researchguidesindex.asp
  Click title
- Divorce Records in England and Wales after 1858
  www.nationalarchives.gov.uk/catalogue/researchguidesindex.asp
  Click title
- Resources: Divorce and Matrimonial Causes
  www.findmypast.com/resources/divorcematrimonialcauses/
  Databases; pay per view

Domesday Book

- Domesday Book
  www.nationalarchives.gov.uk/catalogue/researchguidesindex.asp
  Click title
- Domesday Book
  www.nationalarchives.gov.uk/documentsonline/domesday.asp
  Digitised images; fee-based
- The Domesday Book Online
  www.domesdaybook.co.uk
  General discussion

Ecclesiastical Records *see* Church Records

Ecclesiastical Visitations

- Episcopal Visitation Returns 1744 and 1779
  www.foda.org.uk/visitations/intro/introduction1.htm
  Transcript of Devon returns

Educational Records *see also* School Records

- Sources for the History of Education
  www.nationalarchives.gov.uk/nra/guides/
  Click title. Listed in the National Register of Archives
- An Outline of Sources for the History of Education in London
  Metropolitan Archives
  www.cityoflondon.gov.uk/Corporation/leisure_heritage/
  libraries_archives_museums_galleries/lma/
  visitor_information/free_information_leaflets.htm
  Click title

Electoral Registers *see also* Absent Voters Lists
- Electoral Registers
  www.familyrecords.gov.uk/frc/pdfs/electoral_registers.pdf
  Brief
- United Kingdom Electoral Registers and their Uses
  www.bl.uk/collections/social/spis_er.html
- Official Electoral Roll Online
  www.eroll.co.uk
  Electoral registers, 2003-7

Durham
- Durham County Record Office: Register of Electors
  www.durham.gov.uk/recordoffice/usp.nsf/lookup/
  pdfhandlists/$file/userguide06.pdf

Kent
- Maidstone, Kent 1832 Electoral Register
  freepages.genealogy.rootsweb.com/~mrawson/poll1832.html
  For 1845 see /poll1845.html

London & Middlesex
- Electoral Registers at London Metropolitan Archives
  www.cityoflondon.gov.uk/Corporation/leisure_heritage/
  libraries_archives_museums_galleries/lma/
  visitor_information/free_information_leaflets.htm
  Click title

Yorkshire
- Electoral Registers
  www.calderdale.gov.uk/wtw/sources/sourcetypes/
  elec_registers.html
  Digitised registers for Halifax, 1832-90

Glamorganshire
- Glamorgan Record Office: Electoral Registers
  www.glamro.gov.uk/adobe/ELECTORAL%20REGISTERS.pdf
  General discussion, with details of registers held

Enclosure Awards
- Enclosure Awards
  www.nationalarchives.gov.uk/catalogue/researchguidesindex.asp
  Click title

Bedfordshire
- Inclosure Records: Introduction
  www.bedfordshire.gov.uk/CommunityAndLiving/
  ArchivesAndRecordOffice/GuidesToCollections/
  InclosureRecordsIntroduction.aspx
  In Bedfordshire

Berkshire
- New Landscapes: Enclosure in Berkshire
  www.berkshireenclosure.org.uk
  Digitised images of Berkshire enclosure maps and awards

Estate Agents Records
- Estate Agents Records: guide to collections
  www.bedfordshire.gov.uk/CommunityAndLiving/
  ArchiveAndRecordOffice/GuidestoCollections/
  EstateAgentsRecords.aspx
  In Bedfordshire

Estate Records *see also* Deeds Registries, Manorial Records, *and* Title Deeds
- England: How to Use Land Records
  www.familysearch.org
  Click 'search', 'research helps', and 'E' (for England), and scroll down to title

Bedfordshire
- Estate Correspondence
  www.bedfordshire.gov.uk/CommunityAndLiving/
  ArchivesAndRecordOffice/GuidesToCollections/
  EstateCorrespondence.aspx
  In Bedfordshire

Essex
- Estate Records
  linux02.lib.cam.ac.uk/earlscolne/reference/index.htm#estate
  Discussion based on the records of Earls Colne, Essex

London & Middlesex
- Historical Gazetteeer of London before the Great Fire: Cheapside; parishes of All Hallows, Honey Lane, St. Martin Pomary, St. Mary Le Bow, St. Mary Colechurch, and St.Pancras, Soper Lane
  www.british-history.ac.uk/sources.asp?pubid=8
  History of the descents of property

Family Bibles
- Bible Records Online
  www.biblerecords.com
  Family history entries found in bibles; some English entries

Feet of Fines
- Land Conveyances: Feet of Fines 1182-1833
  www.nationalarchives.gov.uk/catalogue/researchguidesindex.asp
  Click title
- Public Records: Feet of Fines
  www.medievalgenealogy.org.uk/fines/index.shtml

Buckinghamshire
- A Calendar of the Feet of Fines for the County of Buckingham, 7 Richard I to 44 Henry III
  www.buckscc.gov.uk/brr__volumes/04.pdf
  Digitised images of a Buckinghamshire Record Society volume

Lancashire
- Local History: Feet of Fines
  www.british-history.ac.uk/subject.asp?subject=5&gid=90
  For Lancashire, 1189-1558, Yorkshire, 1486-1603, and Lincolnshire, 1244-1272. From record society publications

Lincolnshire *see* Lancashire

Yorkshire *see* Lancashire

Field Books
- Field Book of Walsham le Willows
  content.ancestry.com/iexec/?htx=List&dbid=7557
  Subscription required

Fire Insurance Records
- Fire Insurance Records at Guildhall Library
  www.history.ac.uk/gh/fire.htm
- The 'Place in the Sun' Project: using the online index of Sun Fire Office Policy Registers 1811-35
  www.history.ac.uk/gh/sun.htm
- Index of the Surrey Entries in the Sun Insurance Office Fire Insurance Registers 1788-93
  www.surreyarchaeology.org.uk/slhc/fire.html

Flood Claims
- Sheffield Flood Claims Archive
  extra.shu.ac.uk/sfca
  Records of 7000 claimants from the Dale Dyke Dam disaster

Freeholders Lists
- Devon Freeholders 1711-1799
  www.foda.org.uk/freeholders/
  List of men liable for jury service

Freemen's Records
Chester
- Freemen of Chester Records Online
  www.cheshire.gov.uk/Recordoffice/Freemen/Home.htm
  Freemen 1747-1825

Ipswich
- Freemen of Ipswich, Suffolk
  www.familyhistoryonline.net/database/
  SFKIpswichFreemen.shtml
  Pay per view database

Maidstone
- Maidstone Freeman's Roll 1835
  freepages.genealogy.rootsweb.com/≈mrawson/free1835.html

Gazettes

- Gazettes Online
  www.gazettes-online.co.uk
  Indexes of the official gazettes published in London, Belfast and Edinburgh for the 20th c.

Glebe Terriers

- Glebe Terriers
  www.bedfordshire.gov.uk/CommunityAndLiving/
  ArchivesAndRecordOffice/GuidesToCollections/
  GlebeTerriers-Introduction.aspx

  For Bedfordshire

Hearth Tax

- Hearth Tax 1662-1688
  www.nationalarchives.gov.uk/catalogue/researchguidesindex.asp
  Click title
- The British Record Society: the Hearth Tax
  www.britishrecordsociety.org.uk/hearthtax.htm
- The British Academy Hearth Tax Project
  www.roehampton.ac.uk/hearthtax/
- The Hearth Tax (1662-1666, 1669-1674)
  www.progenealogists.com/greatbritain/hearthtax.htm
  Includes links to many transcripts

London & Middlesex

- London: Taxation Records (Hearth Tax)
  www.british-history.ac.uk/place.asp?gid=54&region=1
  Transcript of returns for 1662-3 & 1666

Oxfordshire

- The 1662 Hearth Tax Returns for Ploughley Hundred area in Oxfordshire
  www.whipple.org/oxford/
  ploughley_100_hearth_tax_1662.html

Warwickshire

- Hearth Tax Return for Warwick Town 1670
  www.hunimex.com/warwick/hearth_1670.html

Heraldic Visitations

- Heralds Visitations and the College of Arms
  www.medievalgenealogy.org.uk/guide/vis.shtml
- The Harleian Society
  harleian.co.uk
  Publishers of heraldic visitations and parish registers (mainly London)
- The Heralds Visitations of the West Country
  www.uk-genealogy.org.uk/visitations/
  Databases from the published visitations of the Harleian Society for Berkshire, Cornwall, Devon, Dorset, Gloucestershire, Kent, Norfolk, Somerset, Wiltshire, Worcestershire.

Bedfordshire

- Visitations of Bedfordshire 1566, 1582 and 1634
  content.ancestry.com/iexec/?htx=List&dbid=7775
  Subscription required

Cumberland

- Cumberland, England Visitations 1615
  content.ancestry.com/iexec/?htx=List&dbid=6591
  Subscription required

Devon

- Devon, England Visitations 1620
  content.ancestry.com/iexec/?htx=BookList&dbid=6618
  Subscription required

Dorset

- Visitation of Dorset 1623
  content.ancestry.com/iexec/?htx=List&dbid=7778
  Subscription required

Hertfordshire

- Visitation of Hertfordshire 1572 and 1634
  content.ancestry.com/iexec/?htx=List&dbid=7776
  Subscription required

Lancashire

- Lancashire, England: Visitations 1567
  content.ancestry.com/iexec/?htx=List&dbid=6478
  Subscription required

London
- Visitation of London 1633-1635
  content.ancestry.com/iexec/?htx=List&dbid=7405
  Subscription required

Norfolk
- Visitations of Norfolk 1563 and 1613
  content.ancestry.com/iexec/?htx=List&dbid=7781
  Subscription required

Nottinghamshire
- Nottinghamshire, England,: Visitations
  content.ancestry.com/iexec/?htx=List&dbid=6621
  Subscription required

Oxfordshire
- Oxfordshire, England, Visitations 1566, 1574 and 1634
  content.ancestry.com/iexec/?htx=List&dbid=6596
  Subscription required

Somerset
- Somerset, England, Visitations 1623
  content.ancestry.com/iexec/?htx=List&dbid=6607
  Subscription required

Worcestershire
- Visitation of Worcester 1569
  content.ancestry.com/iexec/?htx=List&dbid=7782
  Subscription required

Montgomeryshire
- Pedigrees of Montgomeryshire Families 1711-1712
  content.ancestry.com/iexec/?htx=List&dbid=7969
  Subscription required

Hospital Records
- Hospital Records Database: a joint project of the Wellcome Trust and The National Archives
  www.nationalarchives.gov.uk/hospitalrecords/
- Hospital Records
  www.bedfordshire.gov.uk/CommunityAndLiving/ArchivesAndRecordOffice/
  In Bedfordshire. Click 'Guides to Collections' and title.
- Hospital Records
  www.cityoflondon.gov.uk/Corporation/leisure_heritage/libraries_archives_museums_galleries/lma/visitor_information/free_information_leaflets.htm
  Click title. In London Metropolitan Archives

Inquisitions Post Mortem
- Inquisitions Post Mortem, Henry III - Charles I: Landholders and their Heirs
  www.nationalarchives.gov.uk/catalogue/researchguidesindex.asp
  Click title
- Public Records: Inquisitions Post Mortem
  www.medievalgenealogy.org.uk/guide/ipm.shtml

Gloucestershire
- Abstracts of Gloucestershire Inquisitions Post Mortem returned into the Court of Chancery in the Reign of King Charles the First
  content.ancestry.com/iexec/?htx=BookList&dbid=28533
  Subscription required

Insurance Records *see also* Marine Insurance Records
- Fire Insurance Records at Guildhall Library
  www.history.ac.uk/gh/fire.htm
- The Place in the Sun Project: using the online index of Sun Fire Office Policy Registers 1816-33
  www.history.ac.uk/gh/sun.htm

International Genealogical Index
- International Genealogical Index
  www.familysearch.org
  Click 'Search' and title. Make sure you read the 'tips' page before searching.
- Help: International Genealogical Index
  www.familysearch.org/eng/helps/Search/Ancestors/igisearch.htm

- International Genealogical Index
  www.genuki.org.uk/big/eng/LIN/igi.html
  General discussion of what is one of the most-used family history indexes
- International Genealogical Index and Sources in Mormon Family History Centres
  www.history.ac.uk/gh/igi.htm
- Finding LDS Batch Numbers
  www.genuki.org.uk/big/FindingBatchNos.html
  For using the I.G.I
- IGI Batch Numbers: British Isles and North America
  freepages.genealogy.rootsweb.com/~hughwallis/
  IGIBatchNumbers.htm

Interregnum Land Records
- Crown, Church and Royalist Lands, 1642-1660
  www.nationalarchives.gov.uk/catalogue/researchguidesindex.asp
  Click title

Jacobite Records
- The Jacobite Risings 1715 and 1745
  www.nationalarchives.gov.uk/catalogue/researchguidesindex.asp
  Click title

Justicing Notebooks
- Justice in eighteenth-century Hackney: the justicing notebook of Henry Norris and the Hackney Petty Sessions Book
  www.british-history.ac.uk/source.asp?pubid=237
  Digitised copy of a London Record Society publication, 1991.

Land Tax
Devon
- Shirwell Land Tax
  genuki.cs.ncl.ac.uk/DEV/Shirwell/landTax/index.html
- Stoke Rivers Land Tax Records
  genuki.cs.ncl.ac.uk/DEV/StokeRivers/LandTax/index.html
  Annual assessments, 1780-1832

London
- Land Tax Assessments for the City of London at Guildhall Library
  www.history.ac.uk/gh/landtax.htm
  Of general value, as well as of London interest

Sussex
- Land Tax for Billingshurst, Sussex (1780-1832)
  www.familyhistoryonline.net/database/
  SSXBillingshurstLandTax.shtml
  Pay per view database

Manorial Records
- Manorial and Franchisal Courts
  paleo.anglo-norman.org/court1.html
  Introduction
- Manorial Surveys
  paleo.anglo-norman.org/surveys.html
  Introduction
- Manor Courts & Related Materials
  www.keele.ac.uk/depts/hi/resources/manor_courts/
  Includes a detailed bibliography and select word list
- The Manorial Documents Register and Manorial Lordships
  www.nationalarchives.gov.uk/catalogue/researchguidesindex.asp
  Click title
- Manorial Records
  www.bedfordshire.gov.uk/CommunityAndLiving/
  ArchivesAndRecordOffice/
  General introduction. Click 'Guides to Collections' and title.
- Medieval Source Material on the Internet: Manorial Records
  www.medievalgenealogy.org.uk/sources/manorial.shtml
  Links page
- Manorial Records in the National Archives
  www.nationalarchives.gov.uk/catalogue/researchguidesindex.asp
  Click title
- Manor and other Local Court Rolls, 13th century - 1922
  www.nationalarchives.gov.uk/catalogue/researchguidesindex.asp
  Click title

Bedfordshire
- Manorial Records
  www.bedfordshire.gov.uk/CommunityAndLiving/
  ArchivesAndRecordOffice/GuidesToCollections/
  ManorialRecords1ManorandCourt.aspx

Cumberland
- Cumbrian Manorial Records
  www.lancs.ac.uk/fass/projects/manorialrecords/index.htm

Hampshire
- The Stubbington Manorial Records
  www.le.ac.uk/english/pot/stubb/0prelim.html
  paleo.anglo-norman.org/0prelim.html
  13-16th c.

Yorkshire
- Conisbrough Court Rolls
  www.hrionline.ac.uk/conisbrough
  Transcript, 14-15th c., with some later documents
- Medieval Sourcebook: Court Rolls of the Manor of Wakefield
  1274-1297
  www.fordham.edu/halsall/source/1274wakefield-courtrolls.html
- The Manorial Roll of the Isle of Man 1511-1515
  www.isle-of-man.com/manxnotebook/fulltext/manroll

Marine Insurance Records
- Lloyds Marine Insurance Records
  www.liverpoolmuseums.org.uk/maritime/archive/
  displayGuide.aspx?sid=55

Marriage Licences
- Marriage Licence Allegations Index 1694-1850: Vicar General and
  Faculty Office
  www.englishorigins.com/help/aboutbo-mla2.htm
  Over 670,000 names from 'allegations' made to the Archbishop of
  Canterbury. Subscription based
- Faculty Office Marriage Licence Index
  www.sog.org.uk/vg/faculty.htm
  Brief description of indexing project

- Calendar of Marriage Licences issued by the Faculty Office
  1632-1714
  content.ancestry.com/iexec/?htx=BookList&dbid=28551
  Subscription required
- Vicar General Marriage Licence Index
  www.sog.org.uk/vg/vicgen.htm
  Description of an index covering 1701-1850
- Marrying by Licence: Marriage Bonds and Allegations
  www.york.ac.uk/inst/bihr/guideleaflets/
  marriagebondguidance.pdf
  With particular reference to the Northern Province
  A number of sites provide indexes *etc.* to marriage licence bonds
  and allegations for particular places. These are listed in the
  companion volume, *Births, marriages and deaths on the web.* 2
  vols. 2nd ed. F.F.H.S., 2005.

Marriage Registers
- Boyds Marriage Index 1538-1837
  www.englishorigins.com/help/popup-aboutbo-bmi2.htm
  6,400,000 names from many parish registers, country-wide.
  Subscription based
- The Joiner Marriage Index: a marriage index for the North of
  England
  www.joinermarriageindex.co.uk
  Includes many parishes in Cumberland, Derbyshire, Co. Durham,
  Hertfordshire, Leicestershire, Lincolnshire, Northumberland,
  Nottinghamshire, Westmorland and Yorkshire.

Numerous other sites provide indexes and transcripts of marriage
registers for particular counties and parishes. These are listed in the
companion volume, *Births, marriages and deaths on the web.* 2 vols.
2nd ed. F.F.H.S., 2005.

Midwives Registers
- Central Midwives Board Register of Cases, 1906-1927
  www.genuki.org.uk/big/wal/GA/Llangiwg/Cwmgors/
  MargaretDavies.html
  Midwives' register from Cwmgors, Glamorganshire

Militia Surveys

Suffolk

- Babergh Hundred Military Survey of 1522
  content.ancestry.co.uk/iexec/?htx=List&dbid=7546
  Subscription required

Jersey

- General Don's Militia Survey of 1815
  www.societe-jersiaise.org/alexgle/Don.html
  Brief discussion of a listing of adult males in Jersey

Monumental Inscriptions

Numerous transcripts and indexes of monumental inscriptions for particular places can be found through the gateways listed in chapter 1. Only sites of national importance are listed here.

- Funeral Monuments
  www.medievalgenealogy.org.uk/guide/fun.shtml
- Interment.net
  www.interment.net
  International collection
- Monumental Inscriptions for Family Historians
  www.british-genealogy.com/resources/graves/
  Includes a page on 'recording monumental inscriptions'.
- National Index of Memorial Inscriptions: Guidance Notes
  www.norfolkfhs.org.uk/projects/monumentguide.htm
  How to record inscriptions
- Gravestone Photograph Resources
  www.gravestonephotos.com
- Saving Graves
  www.savinggraves.org
  International site
- Tombstones & Monumental Inscriptions
  www.framland.pwp.blueyonder.co.uk
  Links page
- Transcribing Monumental Inscriptions
  www/gravematters.org.uk/
- Transcribing Monumental Inscriptions
  www.shotover.clara.net/mi.htm

Motor Vehicle Registration

- Plymouth Motor Vehicle Registrations
  www.plymouth.gov.uk/homepage/leisureandtourism/
       archives/archivecatalogues/motorvehicleregistrations.htm

Municipal Records

Bedford

- Bedford Borough Records: Introduction
  www.bedfordshire.gov.uk/CommunityAndLiving/
       ArchivesAndRecordOffice/
  Click 'Guide to Collections' and title. There are also pages on the records of Dunstable and Luton

Cardiff

- Local History: Cardiff Records
  www.british-history.ac.uk/subject.asp?subject=5&gid=92

Dunstable see Bedford

Dunwich

- Bailiffs Minute Book of Dunwich 1404-1430
  content.ancestry.co.uk/iexec/?htx=BookList&dbid=7560
  Subscription required

Hull

- Hull City Archives
  www.sp12.hull.ac.uk/navig/khro.htm
  Transcripts of municipal records

Ipswich

- The Town Finances of Elizabethan Ipswich
  content.ancestry.co.uk/iexec/?htx=List&dbid=7551
  Subscription required. Accounts, 1559-1602.

London

- City of London Calendar of Plea and Memoranda Rolls
  www.british-history.ac.uk/source.asp?gid=60
  From published City archives, 1323-1412

- Calendar of Early Mayor's Court Rolls 1298-1307
  www.british-history.ac.uk/sources.asp?pubid=175
  Transcript from a book published in 1924
- London, City of, Calendar of Letter Books
  www.british-history.ac.uk/place.asp?gid=58&region=1
  13th c.

Luton see Bedford

York
- Extracts from the Municipal Records of the City of York during the Reigns of Edward IV, Edward V and Richard III
  content.ancestry.co.uk/iexec/?htx=BookList&dbid=29674
  Subscription required
- York Bridgemasters Accounts
  www.yorkarchaeology.co.uk/bridgemasters/
  www.iadb.co.uk/bridgemasters/
  Many 15th c. names

National Farm Survey
- National Farm Survey of England and Wales, 1940-1943
  www.nationalarchives.gov.uk/catalogue/
  researchguidesindex.asp
  Click title

Naturalization Records
- Naturalisation and Citizenship: Grants of British Nationality
  www.nationalarchives.gov.uk/catalogue/researchguidesindex.asp
  Click title
- English Denization Records
  www.genealogy-quest.com/naturalization/index.html
  Covers 1690, 1693 & 1694

Newspapers & Journals
- British Library Newspapers
  www.bl.uk/collections/newspapers.html
  Includes details of newspaper digitisation project, and of the Online Newspaper Archive, *etc.*

- United Kingdom Periodicals and Newspapers
  www.ancestry.com/search/locality/dbpage.aspx?tp=3257
  Click title. Collection of indexes to various newspapers. Subscription required
- Newsplan
  www.bl.uk/collections/nplan.html
  Newspaper microfilming project; lists newspaper holdings throughout the UK
- [Newspaper Names Index (South West of England)]
  www.paulhyb.homecall.co.uk/index2.htm
  Index to 18-19th c. newspapers from Somerset, Dorset, Devon and Cornwall
- Internet Library of Early Journals
  www.bodley.ox.ac.uk/ilej/
  Includes digitized copies of the *Gentleman's Magazine, Notes and queries, etc.*
- Edina Index to the *Times*, 1785-1980
  edina.ac.uk/times-index/
  Subscription required
- Historical Newspapers
  history.chadwyck.co.uk
  Commercial services providing full text access to the *Times,* 1785-1870
- Historical Newspaper Collection
  www.ancestry.co.uk/search/rectype/periodicals/news/
  Subscription required
- War *Times* Index
  www.wartimesindex.co.uk
  Index to soldiers mentioned in the *Times,* 1854-1902 who were killed, wounded or missing in action, died from disease, awarded medals, or published personal letters from the front line

Berkshire
- *Windsor and Eton Express* Master Index
  freepages.genealogy.rootsweb.com/~dutillieul/
  ZWindsorEtonExpress/IndexWindsor&Eton.html

Cornwall
- Cornwall Library Service: Cornish Newspaper and Periodical Holdings
  db.cornwall.gov.uk/librarydb/info/newspaper.asp

- The *West Briton and Cornwall Advertiser*: Newspaper Abstracts and Extracts
  freepages.genealogy.rootsweb.com/~wbritonad/
  For the mid-19th century

Gloucestershire
- Gloucestershire Newspapers: a guide to national & local newspapers and their holdings
  www.gloucestershire.gov.uk/index.cfm?articleid=10907

Hampshire
- Anglers Rest Genealogical Indexes
  freespace.virgin.net/anglers.rest/index.htm
  Click title. Mainly a collection of newspaper indexes for Surrey and Hampshire

Kent
- Kent Genealogy: Newspaper Indexes
  freepages.genealogy.rootsweb.com/~newspaper.html
  Indexes to various newspapers

Lancashire
- MLFHS Crematorium Obituary Database
  www.mlfhs.org.uk
  Click 'On-line Data'. Index of newspaper obituary notices, Manchester area
- Old Mersey Times
  www.old-merseytimes.co.uk/
  Numerous extracts of genealogical interest from Liverpool newspapers
- Rochdale Newspaper Index
  libraries.rochdale.gov.uk/ipac20/ipac.jsp?profile=dial-4
  Index of cuttings

Surrey *see also* Hampshire
- Newspaper Detectives
  www.newspaperdetectives.co.uk
  Index, 1864-7 & 1872, to the *Surrey Advertiser*. Later years in progress

- Family Announcements from *Camberley news*
  www.wsfhs.org/FamilyAnnouncements.htm
  Details of an offline index

Wiltshire
- Richard Heaton's Local Newspaper Master Index
  freepages.genealogy.rootsweb.com/~dutillieul/ZOtherPapers/
  Index.html

  Transcripts from mainly Wiltshire newspapers

Yorkshire
- Death Notices in Yorkshire Newspapers
  homepage.ntlworld.com/jeffery.knaggs/YD.html
  Currently for 1901 only
- Harrogate People and Places
  harrogatepeopleandplaces.info
  Index and extracts from Harrogate newspapers

Wales
- Cambrian Index Online
  www.swansea.gov.uk/index.cfm?articleid=5673
  Index to the *Cambrian* newspaper, 19-20th c.

Nonconformist Registers
- England: How to Use Nonconformist Church Records
  www.familysearch.org
  Click 'search', 'research help', and 'E' (for England); then scroll down to title
- BMD Registers
  www.bmdregisters.co.uk
  Digitised nonconformist registers. Pay per view

There are many sites with transcripts and indexes of nonconformist registers. These are listed in the companion volume, *Births, marriages and deaths on the web*. 2 vols. 2nd ed. F.F.H.S., 2005.

Oath Rolls
- Oath Rolls and Sacrament Certificates after 1660
  www.nationalarchives.gov.uk/catalogue/researchguidesindex.asp
  Click title
- Devon and Exeter Oath Rolls 1723
  www.foda.org.uk/oaths/intro/introduction1.htm

Parish Magazines
- Yesterdays Names
  www.yesterdaysnames.co.uk/
  Index of Victorian parish magazines

Parish Records
- Parish Records: Introduction
  **www.bedfordshire.gov.uk/CommunityAndLiving/
      ArchivesAndRecordOffice/GuidesToCollections/
            ParishRecordsIntroductin.aspx**
- Parish and Workhouse Records
  **www.westminster.gov.uk/libraries/archives/
            family-history/parish-records.cfm**
  With particular reference to Westminster

Parish Registers
Many parish register transcripts and indexes are listed in the companion volume in this series, *Births, Marriages and deaths on the Web*. 2 vols. 2nd ed. F.F.H.S., 2005. Only sites of general importance are listed here.
- England: How to Use Church Records 1538 to the Present
  www.familysearch.org
  Click 'search', 'research helps', 'E' (for England), and scroll down to title. There are also separate pages on christenings, marriages and burials
- Family History for Beginners: Parish Registers
  www.mlfhs.org.uk/Infobase/Begin-Registers.htm
  Basic introduction
- English Parish Registers
  www.british-genealogy.com/resources/registers/indexf.htm
- Free Reg
  freereg.rootsweb.com
  Includes pages on English parish registers
- Parish records in England and Wales
  globalgenealogy.com/globalgazette/gazfd/gazfd28.htm
  Actually about parish <u>registers</u>, despite the title
- County and Country sources: Introduction
  www.sog.org.uk/prc/intro.shtml
  Includes lists of parish register transcripts held

- Parish Registers
  www.parishregisters.co.uk
  Collection of transcripts from various counties
- Bob Holloways Genealogy Page for Source Information: Parish Register Details
  members.aol.com/aisling13/ixparish.htm
  Links to transcripts *etc.,* now very out of date
- Parish Register Transcription Society
  www.prtsoc.org.uk
  Publisher of parish registers for Hampshire, Norfolk, Sussex, *etc.*
- Resources: Parish Registers
  www.findmypast.com/resources/parish/
- Family Relatives.com Parish Records Index
  www.familyrecords.com/information/info__detail.php?id=49
  List of 1500 parish registers available (mainly marriages from the Phillimore series). Pay per view
- From Fleet Street to Gretna Green: the reform of 'clandestine marriage' under Lord Chancellor Hardwicke's Marriage Act of 1753
  www.geocities.com/Athens/Aegean/7023/clandestine.html
- The Goldmine of Dade Registers
  www.pontefractfhs.org.uk/Dade__registers.htm
  Discussion of very detailed registers found mainly in the Diocese of York

Wales
- The Parish Registers of Wales
  www.genuki.org.uk/big/wal/ParishRegs.html
  General introduction

Passenger Lists
- Passenger Lists on the Internet
  members.aol.com/rprost/passenger.html
  Gateway; mainly concrening ships that sailed to North America
- Ancestors on Board
  www.ancestorsonboard.com
  Digitised images of UK outbound passenger lists, 1890-1960. Pay per view
- Resources; Passenger Lists Leaving UK 1890-1960
  www.findmypast.com/resources/passengerlists/
  Database; pay per view

- English & Welsh roots: getting from here to there
  globalgenealogy.com/globalgazette/gazfd/gazfd24.htm
  Primarily a discussion of passenger lists
- Immigrant Ship Transcribers Guild
  www.immigrantships.net
- The Ships List
  www.theshipslist.com/
- Official Records of Passengers
  www.liverpoolmuseums.org.uk/maritime/archive/
                              displayGuide.aspx?sid=36
- Passenger Lists
  www.nationalarchives.gov.uk/catalogue/researchguidesindex.asp
  Click title
- Passenger Lists
  www.lr.org
  Search for title; Lloyds Register information sheet
- Ship Passenger Lists: Hugh Reekie's Index of Indexes
  members.allstream.net/~max-com/Ships.html
  Links to numerous indexes etc.

Canada
- Nanaimo Family History Society Passenger List Indexing Project
  members.shaw.ca/nanaimo.fhs/
  Early 20th c passenger arrivals in Quebec

New Zealand
- New Zealand Bound
  freepages.genealogy.rootsweb.com/~nzbound/
  Passenger list pages
- Passenger Lists
  freepages.genealogy.rootsweb.com/~ourstuff/
                              OurPassengerLists.htm
  To New Zealand

South Africa
- South African Passenger Lists Home Page
  sa-passenger-list.za.net

United States
- Immigration and Ships Passenger Lists Research Guide
  home.att.net/%7Earnielang/shipguide.html

- New York Passenger Lists Quick Guide 1820-1957
  www.genosearch.com/newyork
- Passenger Lists
  www.newenglandancestors.org/education/articles/research/
                      special_topics/passenger/passenger_lists_main.asp
  Detailed discussion of arrivals in New England, 17-19th c.

Passport Records
- Passport Records
  www.nationalarchives.gov.uk/catalogue/researchguidesindex.asp
  Click title
- Resources: Passport Applications
  www.findmypast.com/resources/passportapplications/
  Pay per view database

Phone Books
- British Phone Books 1880-1984
  www.ancestry.co.uk/iexec/?htx=1025
  Subscription required

Photographs
- Dating Old Photographs
  genealogy.about.com/cs/photodating
  Links page
- Victorian and Edwardian Photographs
  www.rogerco.freeserve.co.uk
- The Cambridgeshire Collection: the J.Palmer Clarke / Ramsey & Muspratt Portrait Collection
  hipweb.cambridgeshire.gov.uk/cambscoll/indexRM.html
  Online collection of photographic portraits
- The Hughes Collection
  www.thehughescollection.co.uk
  c.2000 portrait photos from Bromsgrove

Pollbooks
- Poll Books
  www.british-genealogy.com/resources/info/pollbooks.html
- Raymonds Original Pollbooks
  www.stuartraymond.co.uk
  Facsimiles for sale. Click 'pollbooks'

- Poll Books
  ahds.ac.uk/history/collections/pollbooks.htm
  Digitised data from various counties available offline
- English Electoral Polls from the 18th Century
  freepages.genealogy.rootsweb.com/~pobjoyoneill/ENGPOLLS/
  engpolls.htm
  Index to pollbooks for Buckinghamshire 1784, Sussex 1734, and Wiltshire 1772

Bedfordshire
- Pollbook of Bedfordshire 1722
  www.rabancourt.co.uk/abacus/p1722h.html
  people.pwf.cam.ac.uk/jld1/family/p1722h.html
  Transcript
- Pollbook of Bedfordshire 1784
  www.rabancourt.co.uk/abacus/p1784h.html
  people.pwf.cam.ac.uk/jld1/family/p1784h.html

Dorset
- Dorset Poll Book 1807
  www.thedorsetpage.com/Genealogy/info/poll_book.htm

Lancashire
- Liverpool Poll Book 1832
  www.liverpool-genealogy.org.uk/1832Pollbook/
  Pollbook1832.htm

London & Middlesex
- London pollbook, 1713
  www.british-history.ac.uk/report.asp?compid=38807
  From a London Record Society publication
- Westminster Poll Book 1749
  www.hamersleyfamily.com/westminsterpollbook1749.htm
  Index of 9300 names

Nottinghamshire
- 1754 Poll Book for the Town of Nottingham
  www.charliespage.co.uk/pollbookindex.htm

Yorkshire
- Barnsley Poll Book 1835
  www.barnsleyfhs.co.uk/1835a-c.htm
  Continued on 5 further pages
- The Poll Book of the Wakefield Borough Election, Wednesday 12th June 1865
  www.wakefieldfhs.org.uk/Poll%20Book%201865.shtml

Poor Law Records *see also* Parish Records, *and* Settlement Examinations
- The Poor and the Poor Laws
  www.nationalarchives.gov.uk/catalogue/researchguidesindex.asp
  Click title
- Poor Law Records 1834-1871
  www.nationalarchives.gov.uk/catalogue/researchguidesindex.asp
  Click title
- Rossbret Workhouse Web Site
  www.institutions.org.uk/workhouses/
- The Workhouse
  www.workhouses.org.uk
  Comprehensive introduction, with lists of workhouses and guide to records.
- Union Finder Database
  www.fourbears.worldonline.co.uk/html/
  union_finder_database.html
  For locating unions and record offices
- Poor Law Unions
  www.institutions.org.uk/poor_law_unions/index.htm
  Gazetteer
- Poor Law Bastardy Papers
  www.genuki.org.uk/big/eng/LIN/poorbastard.html
  Brief guide
- Index to Paupers in Workhouses 1861 (10% sample)
  www.genuki.org.uk/big/eng/Paupers/
  Partial index of a Parliamentary paper

Bedfordshire
- Poor Law Records pre-1834: The Records of the Provision of Poor Relief in Bedfordshire pre 1834
  **www.bedfordshire.gov.uk/CommunityAndLiving/
  ArchivesAndRecordOffice/GuidesToCollections/
  PoorLawRecordspre1834.aspx**
  Also includes pages on Poor Law Unions

Berkshire
- The Berkshire Overseers Project
  www.berksfhs.org.uk/projects/BerkshireOverseersDetails.htm
  Description of a calendar of all Berkshire poor law documents, 1601-1834

Derbyshire
- Derby Workhouse Reports
  **www.familyhistoryonline.net/database/
  DerbysFHSWorkRep.shtml**
  Pay per view

Hampshire
- Paupers Database
  www.iwight.com/library/record%5Foffice/paupers
  For the Isle of Wight

Herefordshire
- Bromyard Workhouse Database 1840
  **www.data-archive.ac.uk/findingData/
  snDescription.asp?sn=3040**

Hertfordshire
- The Poor Law
  www.hertsfhs.org.uk/hfphs49.html
  In Hertfordshire

Lincolnshire
- Poor Laws Bastardy Papers
  www.genuki.org.uk/big/eng/LIN/poorbastard.html
  Brief description

- Lincolnshire Parish Bastardy Cases
  www.familyhistoryonline.net/database/LincsFHSbastard.shtml
  Pay per view database

London & Middlesex
- Poor Law Records in London and Middlesex
  **www.cityoflondon.gov.uk/Corporation/leisure_heritage/
  libraries_archives_museums_galleries/lma/
  visitor_information/free_information_leaflets.htm**
  Click title
- Chelsea Workhouse Registers 1743-69 and 1782-1799
  **www.leedstrinity.ac.uk/histcourse/18thtown/instruct/
  inmates5.htm**
- Victorian London Public Institutions: Workhouses, Hospitals, Lunatic Asylums, Prisons, Barracks, Orphan Asylums, Convents and other principal Charitable Institutions
  www.gendocs.demon.co.uk/institute.html
  List

Nottinghamshire
- Southwell Union Workhouse (1834-1871)
  www.nationalarchives.gov.uk/documentsonline/workhouse.asp
  Pay per view

Suffolk
- Poor Relief in Elizabethan Ipswich
  content.ancestry.com/iexec/?htx=List&dbid=7465
  Subscription required

Glamorganshire
- Glamorgan Record Office Records of Poor Relief
  www.glamro.gov.uk/adobe/poor1.pdf
  Glamorganshire records

Portraits *see also* Photographs
- National Portrait Gallery
  www.npg.org.uk/live/search/asearch.asp
  Indexes sitters and artists of portraits held

Postcards

- Practical Research Indexes
  www.practicalresearchindexes.co.uk
  Includes offline index to names on postcards

Probate Records *see also* Death Duty Registers

- British Record Society
  www.britishrecordsociety.org.uk
  Publishers of indexes to probate records
- England: How to Use pre-1858 Probate Records
  www.familysearch.org
  Click 'search', 'research helps', 'E' (for England), and scroll down to title
- England: How to Use Probate Records from 1858 to the Present
  www.familysearch.org
  Click 'search', 'research helps', 'E' (for England), and scroll down to title
- England: How to Use Principal Registry wills for 1858 to 1925
  www.familysearch.org
  Click 'search', 'research helps', 'E' (for England) and scroll down to title.
- England: How to Use District Registry Wills for 1858 to 1925
  www.familysearch.org
  Click 'search', 'research helps', 'E' (for England), and scroll down to title
- Pre-1858 Probate in England and Wales: tips for distance research
  www.ancestry.com/library/view/news/articles/2630.asp
- Wills and Probate Records
  www.nationalarchives.gov.uk/catalogue/researchguidesindex.asp
  Click title
- Probate Records and Family History
  www.hmcourts-service.gov.uk/cms/1183.htm
- Wills
  www.medievalgenealogy.org.uk/guide/wil.shtml
- Wills and Death Duty Records after 1858
  www.nationalarchives.gov.uk/catalogue/researchguidesindex.asp
  Click title
- Wills before 1858: where to start
  www.nationalarchives.gov.uk/catalogue/researchguidesindex.asp
  Click title

- Online International Bibliography of Medieval and Early Modern Wills and Probate Inventories
  campus.belmont.edu/honors/WILLBIBHOME.htm
  Lists many individual wills, collections of wills, and works based on probate records
- English Origins of American Colonists
  www.ancestry.co.uk/search/db.aspx?dbid=1038
  Database of 17-18th c. English wills
- Resources: Wills and Probate
  www.findmypast.com/resources/wills/
- Wills
  wills4all.netfirms.com/
  Transcripts of wills submitted by contributors

Prerogative Court of Canterbury

- Prerogative Court of Canterbury Wills (1384-1855)
  www.nationalarchives.gov.uk/documentsonline/wills.asp
  Pay per view site. Important collection of digitised images
- Prerogative Court of Canterbury Wills Index 1750-1800
  www.englishorigins.com/help/popup-aboutbo-pcc2.htm
  208,000 records; in progress. Pay per view
- Wills, Administrations, and other probate records (Prerogative Court of Canterbury 1383-10 January 1858)
  www.nationalarchives.gov.uk/documents/
  ifa__d12__willsandprobate.pdf
- Abstracts of Probate Acts in the Prerogative Court of Canterbury
  content.ancestry.com/iexec/?htx=BookList&dbid=28908
  Subscription required.
- Index to Administrations in the Prerogative Court of Canterbury
  content.ancestry.com/iexec/?htx=BookList&dbid=28564
  Subscription required. For 1649-60

Bank of England

- Bank of England Wills Extracts Index 1717-1845
  www.englishorigins.com/help/popup-aboutbo-boe2.htm
  61,000 names. Pay per view

Berkshire
- Index to Wills Proved and Administrations granted in the Court of the Archdeacon of Berks 1508 to 1652
  content.ancestry.com/iexec/?htx=BookList&dbid=28539
  Subscription required
- Introduction to Abstracts of Probate Documents
  www.genuki.org.uk/big/eng/BRKwills/
  c.1,000 abstracts for Hungerford and Wantage, Berkshire.

Cambridgeshire
- Cambridgeshire Wills Surname Index
  www.cfhs.org.uk/camwisdex.html

Cheshire
- Cheshire County Council: Wills Database Online
  www.cheshire.gov.uk/Recordoffice/Wills/Home.htm
  Index, 1492-1940, of 130,000 wills proved at Chester

Cornwall *see also* Devon
- Calendar of Wills, Administrations and Accounts relating to the Counties of Cornwall and Devon
  content.ancestry.com/iexec/?htx=BookList&dbid=28560
  Subscription required. Proved in the Cornish Archidiaconal Court, 1569-1799
- Probate Courts (pre 1858)
  www.cornwall.gov.uk/index.cfm?articleid=38680
  In Cornwall

Cumberland *see* Lancashire

Devon *see also* Cornwall
- Devon Names in the Calendars of the Prerogative Court of Canterbury Wills to 1700
  www.cs.ncl.ac.uk/genuki/DEV/DevonWills/
- Calendars of Wills and Administrations relating to the Counties of Devon and Cornwall
  content.ancestry.com/iexec/?htx=BookList&dbid=28552
  Subscription required. Index of wills from the Court of the Principal Registry of the Bishop of Exeter 1559-1799, and the Archdeaconry Court of Exeter 1540-1799. The wills themselves were destroyed in the Blitz

- Calendar of Wills and Administrations relating to the Counties of Devon and Cornwall
  content.ancestry.com/iexec/?htx=BookList&dbid=28559
  Subscription required. Index of wills proved in the Consistory Court of the Bishop of Exeter, 1532-1800. The records themselves were destroyed in the Blitz

Durham
- Bringing the Dead to Life: Durham and Northumberland Probate Records 1540-1857
  familyrecords.dur.ac.uk/nei
  Project to digitise and index 150,000 wills

Essex
- Wills of the County of Essex (England). Volume 2. 1565-1571
  www.newenglandancestors.org/research/database/essexwills/
                                                    default.asp
  Subscription required

Gloucestershire & Bristol
- A Calendar of Wills Proved in the Consistory Court (City and Deanery of Bristol Division) of the Bishop of Bristol 1572-1792
  content.ancestry.com/iexec/?htx=BookList&dbid=28543
  Subscription required
- Bristol Wills Index 1793-1858
  www.bristol-city.gov.uk
  Search 'Bristol wills' and click title.

Huntingdonshire
- Calendar of Huntingdonshire Wills 1479-1652
  content.ancestry.com/iexec/?htx=BookList&dbid=28554
  Subscription required

Kent
- Index of Wills and Administrations now preserved in the Probate Registry at Canterbury 1396-1558 & 1640-1650
  content.ancestry.com/iexec/?htx=BookList&dbid=28556
  Subscription required
- Inventories: the Archdeaconry Court of Canterbury Inventory Papers Index for 1660, 1661, 1681, 1689, 1690 and 1699
  freepages.genealogy.rootsweb.com/~mrawson/invent.html
  Index to over 1,000 probate inventories

Lancashire

- An Index of Wills and Related Documents covering Lancashire north of the Ribble, and parts of Cumberland, Westmorland and Yorkshire, 1748-1858
  www.uclan.ac.uk/facs/class/humanities/family/Probate/
  WillIntro.htm

Leicestershire

- Calendars of Wills and Administrations relating to the County of Leicester proved in the Archdeaconry Court of Leicester 1495-1649
  content.ancestry.com/iexec/?htx=BookList&dbid=28547
  Subscription required. Also indexes wills in various peculiar courts
- Index to the Wills and Administrations proved and granted in the Archdeaconry Court of Leicester 1660-1750
  content.ancestry.com/iexec/?htx=BookList&dbid=28557
  Subscription required. Also includes various peculiars

Lincolnshire

- Calendars of Lincoln Wills
  content.ancestry.com/iexec/?htx=BookList&dbid=28548
  Subscription required. Proved in various courts
- Lincoln Consistory Court Wills Index
  www.lincolnshire.gov.uk/archives/section.asp?catId=13105
  For 1701-1800

London & Middlesex

- Wills in London Metropolitan Archives and elsewhere
  www.cityoflondon.gov.uk/Corporation/leisure__heritage/
  libraries__archives__museums__galleries/lma/
  visitor__information/free__information__leaflets.htm
  Click title
- London Signatures
  www.cityoflondon.gov.uk/Corporation/wills/index.htm
  Index of 10,000 Archdeaconry of London wills, and 23,500 Archdeaconry of Surrey marriage bonds
- Probate Records (wills and adminstrations) at Guildhall Library
  www.history.ac.uk/gh/probate.htm
  Primarily relates to the London area. General discussion

- Consistory Court of London Will Abstracts volume 8 (1621-1630)
  www.genuki.org.uk/big/eng/Wills/Wills2.html
  For wills of the Commissary Court of London 1629-34, see /Wills1.html; for 1644/5-1646, /Wills3.html
- Archdeaconry Court of London Wills Index 1700-1807
  www.originsnetwork.com/help/popup-aboutbo-acl.htm
- London Consistory Court Wills 1492-1547
  www.british-history.ac.uk/sources.asp?pubid=573
  Transcript of a London Record Society published volume
- Indexes to Probate Inventories of the Peculiar Court of the Dean and Chapter of St. Paul's Cathedral
  www.history.ac.uk/gh/invent.htm

Norfolk

- Norfolk Record Office Guide to Holdings: Probate Records
  archives.norfolk.gov.uk/guide/nroprob.htm
- Index to Wills Proved in the Consistory Court of Norwich
  content.ancestry.com/iexec/?htx=BookList&dbid=28565
  Subscription required. Covers 1550-1603

Northamptonshire

- Northamptonshire Wills
  www.geocities.com/Heartland/Fields/1759
- Northamptonshire and Rutland Probate Index
  www.familyhistoryonline.net/database/
  NorthantsFHSprobate.shtml
  Pay per view database
- A Calendar of Wills relating to the Counties of Northampton and Rutland proved in the Court of the Archdeacon of Northampton
  content.ancestry.com/iexec/?htx=Booklist&dbid=28534
  Subscription required
- Administrations in the Archdeaconry of Northampton (1667-1710)
  content.ancestry.com/iexec/?htx=BookList&dbid=28563
  Subscription required

Northumberland see Durham

Rutland see Northamptonshire

Shropshire

- Shropshire and Montgomeryshire Wills (1858-1940)
  www.familyhistoryonline.net/database/
  ShropshireFHSwills.shtml
  Pay per view database

Somerset

- Calendar of Wills and Administrations in the Court of the Archdeacon of Taunton 1537-1799
  content.ancestry.com/iexec/?htx=BookList&dbid=28555
  Subscription required
- Estate Duty Wills Search
  www.somerset.gov.uk/archives/
  Click 'Search catalogues & indexes' and 'Index to Somerset wills 1812-1857'

Staffordshire

- Staffordshire Probate (wills and administrations)
  www.familyhistoryonline.net/database/STSProbate.shtml
  Pay per view database. In progress; the initial index covers testators from Burslem.
- Calendar of Wills & Administrations in the Consistory Court of the Bishop of Lichfield and Coventry 1516 to 1652
  content.ancestry.com/iexec/?htx=BookList&dbid=28538
  Subscription required

Suffolk

- Suffolk Probate Indexes 1847-1857
  www.familyhistoryonline.net/database/SFKProbate.shtml
  Pay per view database
- Ipswich Probate Inventories 1583-1631
  content.ancestry.com/iexec/?htx=List&dbid=7512
  Subscription required
- Sudbury Archdeaconry Wills 1439-1638
  content.ancestry.com/iexec/?htx=List&dbid=7608
  Subscription required

Surrey *See also* London and Middlesex

- Surrey Plus Wills Index
  www.rootsweb.com/~engsurry/
  New entries continually being added by contributors

Sussex

- Sussex Will Index
  www.familyhistoryonline.net/database/
  SussexFHGprobate.shtml
  Pay per view
- Sussex Wills Index
  www.sussex-opc.org
  Click wills. Transcripts of wills sent in by contributors

Warwickshire *see* Staffordshire

Westmorland *see* Lancashire

Wiltshire

- Wiltshire Wills Project
  www.wiltshire.gov.uk/leisure-and-culture/access-to-records/
  wiltshire-and-swindon-record-office/
  wsro-wiltshire-wills-project.htm
  Project to index and digitise Wiltshire wills
- Wiltshire Courts Wills Index (1800-1858)
  www.familyhistoryonline.net/database/WiltsIndexWills.shtml
  Pay per view

Worcestershire

- Calendar of Wills and Administrations in the Consistory Court of the Bishop of Worcester
  content.ancestry.com/iexec/?htx=BookList&dbid=28550
  Subscription required. Covers 1451-1652

Yorkshire *see also* Lancashire

- Probate Records
  www.york.ac.uk/inst/bihr/guideleaflets/guideprob.pdf
  At the Borthwick Institute of Historical Research, York. Guide.
- York Medieval Probate Index 1267-1500
  www.originsnetwork.com/help/popup-aboutbo-ymed.htm
  Pay per view
- York Peculiars Probate Index 1383-1883
  www.originsnetwork.com/help/aboutbo-ypec.htm
  Pay per view database

Quaker Records

Buckinghamshire
- The Minute Book of the Monthly Meeting of the Society of Friends for the Upperside of Buckinghamshire 1669-1690
  www.buckscc.gov.uk/brs__volumes/01.pdf
  Digitised images of a Buckinghamshire Record Society volume

Yorkshire
- Yorkshire Quaker Heritage Project
  www.hull.ac.uk/oldlib/archives/quaker/
  Includes research guide, location register of records, and name index to several Yorkshire meetings

Quarter Sessions Records

Kent
- Kent Quarter Sessions Index
  freepages.genealogy.rootsweb.com/~mrawson/sessions.html
  Indexes to various Quarter sessions records, e.g. bastardy orders, higglers licences, removal orders, *etc.*, 17-18th c.

London & Middlesex
- A Brief Guide to the MIddlesex Sessions Records
  www.cityoflondon.gov.uk/Corporation/leisure__heritage/ libraries__archives/museums__galleries/lma/ visitor__information/free__information__leaflets.htm
  Click title

Shropshire
- Shropshire County Quarter Sessions (1831-1920)
  www.familyhistoryonline.net/database/ ShropshireFHSquarter.shtml
  Pay per view database

Wiltshire
- Index of Wiltshire Quarter Sessions Calendars
  www.familyhistoryonline.net/database/WiltsFHSQS.shtml
  Pay per view

Caernarvonshire
Records of the Caernarfonshire Quarter Sessions 1546-1795
www.gtj.org.uk/en/themeitems/10263
Online exhibition of digitised documents

Montgomeryshire
- Montgomeryshire Quarter Sessions
  www.powys.gov.uk/index.php?id=939

Rate Books
- Rate Books for Family History
  www.devon.gov.uk/index/democracycommunities/ neighbourhoods-villages/record__office/family__history__3/ local__tax__records__rates.html

Recognizance Rolls
- Ipswich Recognizance Rolls 1294-1327
  content.ancestry.com/iexec/?htx=BookList&dbid=7475
  Subscription required

Removal Orders *see* Settlement Examinations

Return of Owners of Land
- Return of Owners of Land 1873
  www.uk-genealogy.org.uk/datafiles/landtaxsearch.html
  Index; in progress

Leicestershire
- Return of Owners of Land Index: Leicestershire 1871
  freespace.virgin.net/guy.etchells/RoOLindex.htm
  Also includes Nottinghamshire

Norfolk
- Return of Owners of land in Norfolk in 1873
  www.thornburypump.myby.co.uk/1873/
  Database

Oxfordshire
- Return of Owners of Land 1873: Oxfordshire
  www.genoot.com/eng/oxf/landowners/

Staffordshire
- Staffordshire Landowners 1873
  www.data-archive.ac.uk/findingData/
  snDescription.asp?sn=4509
  Report of a study based on the *Return of owners of land*

Wales
- Returns of Owners of Land 1873 (Scottish, Welsh & Irish)
  www.cefnpennar.com/1873index.htm

Royalist Composition Papers
- Index Nominum to the Royalist Composition Papers
  content.ancestry.com/iexec/?htx=BookList&dbid=28536
  Subscription required

St. Paul's Rebuilding Fund
- Indexes to Parish Returns towards the rebuilding of St. Paul's Cathedral eg. 1678
  www.history.ac.uk/gh/briefs.htm
  List of returns from throughout England, most listing contributors. Names are not indexed; only parishes.

School Records *see also* Educational Records

London & Middlesex
- Records of Christ's Hospital and Bluecoat Schools at Guildhall Library
  www.history.ac.uk/gh/christ1.htm
- Pupil Records of King Edward's Schools at Guildhall Library
  www.history.ac.uk/gh/brhkes.html
- London School Attendance Medals
  www.cityoflondon.gov.uk/Corporation/leisure__heritage/
  libraries__archives__museums__galleries/lma/
  visitor__information/free__information__leaflets.htm
  Click title
- Bow Creek School, Orchard House Place, Leamouth, Poplar: pupil admissions register 1896-1935
  homepage.ntlworld.com/geoff.matt/bowcreek__intro.html

Staffordshire
- Cotton College
  www.freewebs.com/cottoncollege/index.htm
  Roman Catholic seminary in Staffordshire; includes various lists of teachers and students, 1873-1987

Surrey
- Charterhouse Register 1872-1910
  content.ancestry.com/iexec/?htx=List&dbid=7445
  Subscription required. Register of a Godalming, Surrey school

Glamorganshire
- Glamorgan School Admission Registers
  www.familyhistoryonline.net/database/GlamFHSschools.shtml
  Pay per view database; 29,251 entries

Settlement Examinations & Removal Orders

Devon
- Settlement & Removal in Rural Devon Parishes
  genuki.cs.ncl.ac.uk/DEV/DevonMisc/Settlement.html

Lincolnshire
- Lincolnshire Parish Settlement Examinations
  www.familyhistoryonline.net/database/
  LincsFHSsettleExam.shtml
- Lincolnshire Settlement Certificates
  www.familyhistoryonoline.net/database/LincsFHSSetCert.shtml
  Database of 5264 names. Pay per view

London & Middlesex
- St. Martin in the Fields Settlement Examinations Index
  www.westminster.gov.uk/libraries/archives/indexes/
  sett__intro.cfm
  On-line index, covering 1750-75 at present, but more to be added
- St. Luke, Chelsea: Settlement and Bastardy examinations 1733-1750
  www.workhouses.org.uk/index.html?Chelsea/Chelseabar.shtml
  Transcripts

Sussex

- West Sussex Poor Law Database 1662-1835
  www.westsussex.gov.uk/ccm/content/
  libraries-and-archives/record-office
  www.sussexrecordsociety.org/plhome.asp
  Index to settlement examinations and removal orders

Wiltshire

- Wiltshire Removal Orders
  www.familyhistoryonline.net/database/
  WiltshireFHSremovals.shtml
  Database with 20,593 names

State Papers

- State Papers Domestic: Edward VI - Charles I, 1547-1649
  www.nationalarchives.gov.uk/catalogue/researchguidesindex.asp
  Click title. Also sepatate guides for 1642-60, 1660-1714, & 1714-82

Subsidies see also Tax Records

- Public Records: Subsidies and Other Taxes
  www.medievalgenealogy.org.uk/guide/tax.shtml

Cumberland see Yorkshire

Gloucestershire

- Lay Subsidy Roll E179/116/488. Gloucestershire 13 April 1625
  www.genuki.org.uk/big/eng/GLS/LaySubsidy116488.html

Kent

- The Kent Lay Subsidy Roll of 1334/5
  www.kentarchaeology.org.uk/Research/Pub/KRV/18/3/058.htm

Leicestershire

- English Surnames Survey
  www.le.ac.uk/elh/resources/surnames.html
  Various lay subsidies and poll taxes for Leicestershire,
  Lincolnshire, Rutland and Yorkshire

Lincolnshire see Leicestershire

London & Middlesex see also Yorkshire

- Two early London Subsidy Rolls
  www.british-history.ac.uk/source.asp?pubid=11
  For 1292 and 1319. Digitised copy of a London Record Society
  publication, 1951

Rutland see Leicestershire

Shropshire

- Lay Subsidy, Stottesden Hundred, 1661
  www.uk-transcriptions.accessgenealogy.com/
  Stottesden%20Subsidy.htm

Worcestershire

- Worcestershire Lay Subsidy Roll, circ. 1280
  content.ancestry.com/iexec/?htx=List&dbid=7943
  Subscription required

Yorkshire see also Leicestershire

- Local History: Lay Subsidy Records
  www.british-history.ac.uk/subject.asp?subject=5&gid=53
  Includes transcripts from published sources for Yorkshire, 1301,
  Cumberland, 1332, & London, 1292, 1319, 1332, 1541, & 1582

Tax Records see also Hearth Tax, Land Tax, & Subsidies

- Taxes
  www.nationalarchives.gov.uk/familyhistory/guide/people/
  tax.htm
- Taxation Records before 1660
  www.nationalarchives.gov.uk/catalogue/researchguidesindex.asp
  Click title
- E179 Database: Records relating to lay and clerical taxation
  www.nationalarchives.gov.uk/e179/
  Lists returns to lay subsidies, hearth tax, etc.

London & Middlesex

- London Inhabitants within the walls 1695
  www.british-history.ac.uk/source.asp?pubid=31
  From a London Record Society publication; record of a duty on
  burials, births and marriages

- Four Shillings in the Pound Aid 1693/4. The City of London, the City of Westminster, and Metropolitan Middlesex
  www.british-history.ac.uk/source.asp?pubid=26

Temperance Records
- The Livesey Collection
  www.uclan.ac.uk/library/usersupport/lrs/collections/livesey/
  index.htm
  Temperance records at the University of Central Lancashire

Terriers
- Terriers and Surveys
  www.bedfordshire.gov.uk/CommunityAndLiving/
  ArchivesAndRecordOffice/GuidesTo Collections/
  TerriersandSurveys.aspx

Tithe Records
- Tithe Records
  www.nationalarchives.gov.uk/catalogue/researchguidesindex.asp
  Click title

Bedfordshire
- Tithe Records
  www.bedfordshire.gov.uk/CommunityAndLiving/
  ArchivesAndRecordOffice/GuidesToCollections/
  TitheRecordsIntroduction.aspx
  Includes list of tithe maps and apportionments for Bedfordshire

Cheshire
- eMapping Victorian Cheshire: Cheshire's Tithe Maps Online
  maps.cheshire.gov.uk/tithemaps/

Devon
- Devon County Council: Tithe Records
  www.devon.gov.uk/index/community/the__county/
  record__office/family__history__3/tithe__records.htm

Dorset
- Dorset Coast Digital Archives
  www.dcda.org.uk
  Click 'interactive maps' and 'tithe apportionments'

Hampshire
- The North Hampshire Tithe Map Project
  www.dutton.force9.co.uk/tithes

London
- The Inhabitants of London in 1638
  www.british-history.ac.uk/source.asp?pubid=176
  From a volume listing householders, compiled for tithe purposes, and published in 1931

Warwickshire
- Warwickshire County Record Office Tithe Apportionments Database
  www.warwickshire.gov.uk/countyrecordoffice
  Click 'On-line catalogue & Databases', and title

Worcestershire
- Worcestershire Tithe and Inclosure Map Project
  worcestershire.whub.org.uk/home/wcc-arch-tithe-maps.html

Yorkshire
- Wakefield District Tithe Awards
  www.familyhistoryonline.net/database/
  WakefieldDFHSTithe.shtml

  Pay per view

Title Deeds *see also* Deeds Registries, Estate Records, & Feet of Fines
- Land Conveyances: Enrolment of Deeds and Registration of Title
  www.nationalarchives.gov.uk/catalogue/researchguidesindex.asp
  Click title
- Deeds Project University of Toronto
  www.utoronto.ca/deeds/research/research.html
  Includes database of medieval Essex deeds
- How to interpret deeds: a simple guide and glossary
  www.britishrecordassociation.org.uk/publication__pages/
  Guidelines3.htm
- How to Interpret Deeds: a Glossary
  www.bedfordshire.gov.uk/CommunityAndLiving/
  ArchivesAndRecordOffice/GuidesToCollections/
  HowToInterpretDeeds.aspx

- Title Deeds
  **www.bedfordshire.gov.uk/CommunityAndLiving/
  ArchivesAndRecordOffice/**
  Click 'Guide to Collections' and title. Brief basic introduction

Toll Books
- Machynlleth Toll Books
  www.genuki.org.uk/big/wal/Machynlleth.html
  Includes index giving the names of buyers and sellers at
  Machynlleth fair in 1632

Tontine Records
- Nominees of the First British Tontine of 1693
  **freepages.history.rootsweb.com/~frpayments/MA1693/
  index.htm**

Trade Directories
- Using Trade Directories in your Research
  www.genealogyreviews.co.uk/tippey_directories.htm
- County Directories
  **www.british-genealogy.com/resources/books/directories/
  index.html**
  Includes a listing of directories known to exist, by county. Not yet
  completed.
- Digital Library of Historical Directories
  www.historicaldirectories.org
  Over 600 digitised trade directories with search facility.
  Important.
- Direct Resources
  www.direct-resources.uk.com
  Index to trade directories of c.1848; nearly 500,000 entries
- English Trade Directories of the 19th Century
  **freepages.genealogy.rootsweb.com/~pobjoyoneill/tradedir/
  engtrade.htm**
  Index to a range of directories for various counties
- British National Directories 1781-1819: an index to places
  www.devon.gov.uk/localstudies/111782/1.html
- Trade Directories Index
  www.achievements.co.uk/services/trade/index.php
  Offline index to 500 directories; fee-based

- United Kingdom Directories & Membership Lists
  www.ancestry.com/search/locality/dbpage.aspx?tp=3257
  Click 'view all 30 U.K. directories'. Collection of trade directory
  databases for various counties. Subscription required
- Trade Directories and Telephone Books at Guildhall Library
  www.cityoflondon.gov.uk/
  Search for 'Guildhall Library guides' and click title. Brief note on
  a major collection
- Pigot's and Slater's topography of the British Isles
  **www.staffs.ac.uk/schools/humanities_and_soc_sciences/
  census/pigot.htm**
  Topographical extracts from various directories. No names.
- UK Directories
  **www.midlandshistoricaldata.org/
  SHPLoader.aspx?x=trade_directories_uk.html**
  Trade directories online, national and West Midlands. Pay per
  view. Also on CD

Buckinghamshire
- Alphabetical Surname Index to Robson's 1839 directory of
  Buckinghamshire
  homepages.rootsweb.com/~mwi/Bucksdir.txt
- Buckinghamshire Historic Trade Directories
  www.buckscc.gov.uk/trade_directories/index.asp
  Indexes to directories, 1782-1832

Cumberland
- Cumbrian Genealogy
  www.btinternet.com/~grigg/
  Index to facsimile and CD editions of trade directories

Derbyshire
- Pigot's Commercial Directory for Derbyshire 1835
  www.genuki.org.uk/big/eng/DBY/Pigot1835/index.html

Devon
- Directory of Devonshire 1830-31 (Pigot & Co's)
  freepages.genealogy.rootsweb.com/~valhender/dir1830.htm
- Directory of Devonshire 1870
  freepages.genealogy.rootsweb.com/~valhender/dir1870.htm
  Morris & Co's directory; incomplete

- Exeter directory, from White's Devonshire directory of 1850
  www.cs.ncl.ac.uk/genuki/DEV/Exeter/White1850.html
- Plymouth Directories
  freepages.genealogy.rootsweb.com/~terryw/
  index.htm#plymouth_directories
  Digitised images of a variety of directories

Gloucestershire
- Forest of Dean: Trade Directories of Gloucestershire
  freepages.genealogy.rootsweb.com/~cbennett/
  Many extracts for particular parishes

Herefordshire
- Genealogy Resources and Documentation
  freepages.genealogy.rootsweb.com/~nmfa/genealogy.html
  Includes trade directories for Herefordshire, 1830 and 1840, and
  for Somerset 1844
- Pigot's Directory of Herefordshire 1835
  www.familyhistoryonline.net/database/PigotsHeref1835.shtml
  Pay per view

Huntingdonshire
- UK Genealogy Archives
  www.uk-genealogy.org.uk/datafiles/tradesearch.html
  Database of *Pigot & Co Directory of Huntingdonshire* 1839. More
  directories will be added

Kent
- Pigots Commercial directory for Kent 1839
  users.ox.ac.uk/~malcolm/genuki/big/eng/KEN/picotken.txt
  Index. Various other indexes are also available by deleting the last
  part of the URL

London & Middlesex
- The Directories of London and the Home Counties
  www.cityoflondon.gov.uk/Corporation/leisure_heritage/
  libraries_archives_museums_galleries/lma/
  visitor_information/free_information_leaflets.htm
  Click title. General introduction with brief discussions of
  particular directories

- London Merchants of 1677
  freepages.history.rootsweb.com/~frpayments/LM1677
  Probably the earliest commercial directory
- *Kent's Directory for the year 1740, containing an alphabetical list
  of the names and places of abode of the directors of public
  companies, persons in publick business, merchants, and other
  eminent trades in the cities of London and Westminster, and the
  Borough of Southwark.* Henry Kent, 1740.
  freepages.history.rootsweb.com/~frpayments/KD1740

Nottinghamshire
- Pigot's 1830 Directory Nottinghamshire
  www.geocities.com/ian_charles_uk/pigots1830index.htm
- Hodson's 1814 Directory Nottingham
  www.geocities.com/ian_charles_uk/1814.htm

Somerset *see also* Herefordshire
- Butcher Cole & Co Directory 1874-5
  www.paulhyb.homecall.co.uk/index4.htm

Staffordshire
- List of UK Trade Directories for Staffordshire, England 1781 to
  1978
  www.northstaffsresearch.co.uk/gene.html

Sussex
- Sussex Online Parish Clerks: Directories of Sussex
  www.sussex-opc.org
  Transcripts of many directories

Warwickshire
- *Lascelles directory of Coventry,* 1850
  www.covfs.org
  Click 'databases'

Westmorland *see* Cumberland

Valuation Office Records
- Valuation Office Records: the Finance (1909-1910) Act
  www.nationalarchives.gov.uk/catalogue/researchguidesindex.asp
  Click title

- 1910-15 Valuation Office Maps and Field Books
  www.nationalarchives.gov.uk/pathways/localhistory/gallery1/
  valuation.htm

Cornwall
- Board of Inland Revenue Land Valuation
  www.cornwall.gov.uk/index.cfm?articleid=38691
  For Cornwall; details of records created under the Finance Act
  1910

Vehicle Licensing Records
- Vehicle Registration and Licensing Records
  www.cityoflondon.gov.uk/Corporation/leisure__heritage/
  libraries__archives__museums__galleries/lma/
  visitor__information/free__information__leaflets.htm
  Click title

War Memorials
Many sites devoted to war memorials are listed in the companion
volume, *War memorials on the web.* 2 vols. F.F.H.S., 2003. Only sites
of national importance are listed here.
- The British War Memorial Project
  www.britishwargraves.org.uk
- The British War Memorial Project
  wargraves.org.uk
- Remembrance & Memorials
  www.stephen-stratford.co.uk/remember.htm
  General pages
- War Memorials Trust
  www.warmemorials.org/
- United Kingdom War Memorials
  www.hellfire-corner.demon.co.uk/memorials.htm
- United Kingdom National Inventory of War Memorials
  www.ukniwm.org.uk
- Commonwealth War Graves Commission
  www.cwgc.org/
  Includes the 'Debt of Honour Register' of those who died in the
  First and Second World War, and in other 20th c. wars, listing
  memorials and graves

- Roll of Honour
  www.roll-of-honour.com/
  Transcripts of memorials from every county

Window Tax *see also* Hearth Tax
- The Window Tax North Westmorland 1777
  www.edenlinks.co.uk/RECORDS/WIN__TAX__NW.HTM
  For South Westmorland, *see* **/WIN-TAX-SW.HTM**

9. Occupational Information

The occupations of our forefathers produced a mass of documentation, which may be of genealogical value. An introduction to web pages based on these sources is provided by:

- United Kingdom and Ireland Occupations
  www.genuki.org.uk/big/Occupations.html

See also:
- Occupations
  www.institutions.org.uk/genealogy/occupations.htm

Historical occupations are listed in:
- Gendocs: Ranks, Professions, Occupations and Trades
  www.gendocs.demon.co.uk/trades.html
  Dictionary of occupations
- Occupations
  www.wakefieldfhs.org.uk/occupations.htm
  Alphabetical list
- A List of Occupations
  myweb.tiscali.co.uk/ticketybol/occupations.htm

For occupations in Bedfordshire, consult:
- Occupations: Archival Sources
  www.bedfordshire.gov.uk/CommunityAndLiving/
      ArchivesAndRecordOffice/Genealogy/Occupations.aspx

For occupations in Wales, consult:
- Wales Occupations
  www.genuki.org.uk/big/wal/Occupations.html

The records of a major institution holding occupational sources are described at:
- Family History at the Modern Records Centre
  www2.warwick.ac.uk/services/library/mrc/subject_guides/
                                            family+history/
  Includes details of records relating to bookbinders, bricklayers,

brushmakers, bus and cab workers, carpenters, carvers, compositors, gilders, house decorators, ironfounders, joiners, miners, painters, picture-frame makers, plasterers, printing workers, quarrymen, seamen, steam engine makers, railwaymen, stonemasons, tramway workers, & woodworkers, *etc.*

For a useful links page, see:
- Occupations
  www.rootsweb.com/≈englin/occupations.htm

Directories of the clergy, of doctors, and of dentists, are included in:
- Directories and Occupations
  www.findmypast.com/Directories.jsp
  Pay per view

Accountants
- Knowledge Guide to Accounting Ancestors
  www.icaew.co.uk/library/index.cfm?AUB=TB21_95412
  Click title. Guide to tracing accountant ancestors

- Records of the Institute of Chartered Accountants in England and Wales and its predecessor bodies at Guildhall Library
  www.history.ac.uk/gh/ghinfo9.htm

Airmen *see also* Seamen
- Tracing Royal Flying Corps and Royal Air Force Ancestry
  www.iwm.org.uk/upload/pdf/famhist_raf2007.pdf
- Family History: Royal Air Force and predecessors
  www.nationalarchives.gov.uk/familyhistory/military/airforce/
- Royal Air Force Museum
  www.rafmuseum.org.uk/
  Includes details of archives held
- Royal Air Force (R.A.F.), R.F.C. & R.N.A.S: First World War, 1914-1918: service records
  www.nationalarchives.gov.uk/catalogue/researchguidesindex.asp
  Click title
- Royal Flying Corps, Royal Naval Air Service, Royal Air Force Register 1914-1919
  www.rfc-rnas-raf-register.org.uk/
  Details of an off-line index

- Royal Air Force: Second World War 1939-1945: Service Records
  www.nationalarchives.gov.uk/catalogue/researchguidesindex.asp
  Click title
- Fleet Air Arm Archive 1939-1945
  www.fleetairarmarchive.net/
  Includes roll of honour, prisoners of war, awards, *etc.*
- The Pilots of 41 Squadron R.A.F., 1939-1945
  brew.clients.ch/RAF41Sqdn.htm
  Includes roll of honour

Apothecaries *see* Medical Men

Apprentices *see also* Liverymen, Seamen (Merchant Navy)
- Apprenticeship records as sources for genealogy
  www.nationalarchives.gov.uk/catalogue/researchguidesindex.asp
  Click title

Lincolnshire
- Lincolnshire Parish Indentures: Apprentices and Masters
  www.familyhistoryonline.net/database/LincsFHSapprentice.shtml
  Pay per view

London & Middlesex
- London Apprenticeship Abstracts 1442-1850
  www.britishorigins.com/help/popup-aboutbo-lonapps.htm
  300,000 names

Architects
- Sources for Architectural History
  www.nationalarchives.gov.uk/nra/guides/
  Click title. Listed in the National Register of Archives

Artists
- Sources for the History of Fine Art and Artists
  www.nationalarchives.gov.uk/nra/guides/
  Click title. Listed in the National Register of Archives
- Artists papers register: a location register of the papers of artists, designers and craftsmen held in publicly accessible collections in the United Kingdom
  www.apr.ac.uk/artists/home.htm
- British Artists
  content.ancestry.co.uk/iexec/?htx=List&dbid=7894
  Subscription required

Attorneys
- Lawyers: records of Attornies and Solicitors
  www.nationalarchives.gov.uk/catalogue/researchguidesindex.asp
  Click title

Bankers & Customers
- Bank of England Archives
  www.bankofengland.co.uk/about/history/archive/index.htm

Bankrupts
- Bankruptcy
  **www.nationalarchives.gov.uk/familyhistory/guide/
  ancestorslaw/bankruptcy.htm**
- Bankrupts and Insolvent Debtors 1710-1869
  www.nationalarchives.gov.uk/catalogue/researchguidesindex.asp
  Click title
- Bankruptcy Records after 1869
  www.nationalarchives.gov.uk/catalogue/researchguidesindex.asp
  Click title

Blacksmiths
- The Blacksmiths Index
  freepages.genealogy.rootsweb.com/≈blacksmiths/

Boatmen *see also* Watermen & Lightermen
- Boatmen, Watermen & Mariners: for ancestors connected with waterways and coastal shipping in Northern England
  townsleyb.members.beeb.net/Boatmen
- Family History: a checklist for researchers
  www.canalmuseum.org.uk/collections/family-history.htm
  Sources for canal boatmen and others connected with waterways
- Virtual Waterways Archive Catalogye
  www.virtualwaterways.co.uk
  Includes family history pages
- The Waterways Archive
  www.thewaterwaystrust.co.uk/museums/archives.shtml

Warwickshire
- Coventry Canal Boat Register
  www.covfhs.org
  Click 'Databases'. Index to register of boats, 1879-1936

Book Trades

- The British Book Trade Index
  www.bbti.bham.ac.uk
- Stationers Hall Copyright Records
  www.nationalarchives.gov.uk/catalogue/researchguidesindex.asp
  Click title
- Stationers and Newspaper Makers Company: Library and Archives
  www.stationers.org/companyhall-libraryandarchives.asp
- Exeter Working Papers in Book History
  bookhistory.blogspot.com/2005/12/index.html

Boxers

- The History of Pre-War Boxing in Britain
  www.prewarboxing.co.uk
  Includes list of boxers, many photographs, *etc.*

Brewers

- Brewery History Society
  breweryhistory.co.uk/
  Includes pages on the society's archives

Brickmakers

- Brickmakers Index: an index of brickfield workers and owners gathered from census, local histories and directories
  www.davidrcufley.btinternet.co.uk/brkindx.htm

Brushmakers

- Society of Brushmakers Descendants
  www.brushmakers.com

Butchers

- History of Guernsey butchers
  history.foote-family.com/butchers/

Cable & Wireless Employees

- Porthcurno Telegraph Museum
  www.porthcurno.org.uk
  Holds personnel records, *etc.*, of Cable & Wireless

Canal Boatmen *see* Boatmen

Carpenters

- Records of the Worshipful Company of Carpenters, volume 1. Apprentices' Entry Books 1654-1694
  www.british-history.ac.uk/sources.asp?pubid=354

Carriers

- Carriers to London Inns and the Turnpike Trusts covering roads to Oxford
  members.aol.com/Rosevearl/titlepg.htm
  Includes lists of carriers and turnpike trustees

Chartists

- Chartist Ancestors
  www.chartists.net
  Database

Chemists

- Biographical Database of the British Chemical Community 1880-1970
  www.open.ac.uk/ou5/Arts/chemists/
  4,780 chemists listed

Circus Performers, *etc.*

- British Fairground Ancestors: Showmen, Circus and Fairground Travellers Index
  users.nwon.com/pauline/Travellers.html
- Circus Historical Society
  www.circushistory.org/
- The Fairground Heritage Trust
  www.fairground-heritage.org.uk
- The National Fairground Archives
  www.nfa.dept.shef.ac.uk
- Two Centuries of Circus People
  www.circusbiography.co.uk
  Project to compile a biographical database

Civil Engineers

- Obituaries of members of the Institution
  nzsghamilton.co.nz/obituaries.htm
  Index to obituaries in the *minutes of proceedings of the Institution of Civil Engineers*

Civil Servants
- Civil Servants Personnel Records
  www.nationalarchives.gov.uk/catalogue/researchguidesindex.asp
  Click title
- Office holders in Modern Britain
  www.british-history.ac.uk/catalogue.asp/type=false&gid=42
  From a published series of books which include volumes devoted to
  treasury officials 1660-1870, officials of the Secretaries of State
  1660-1782, officials of the Boards of Trade 1660-1870, Admiralty
  officials 1660-1870, Home Office officials 1782-1870, Colonial
  Office officials 1794-1870, Foreign Office officials 1782-1870,
  officials of Royal Commissions of Inquiry 1815-1870 & 1870-1939

Clergy
- Biographical Sources for Anglican Clergy
  www.lambethpalacelibrary.org/holdings/Guides/clergyman.html
- Sources for Tracing Clergy and Lay Persons
  www.history.ac.uk/gh/clergy.htm
  Primarily - but not solely - in the Diocese of London
- Clergy of the Church of England Database
  www.theclergydatabase.org.uk
  Currently lists 70,000 names; many more in process
- Fasti Ecclesiae Anglicanae 1066-1300
  www.british-history.ac.uk/catalogue.asp?type=false&gid=39
  Digitised copies of published listings of senior clergy. Continued
  as follows:
      1300-1541 gid=40
      1541-1857 gid=41
- Clergy List 1896
  www.findmypast.com/Directories.jsp
  Click title. Pay per view
- Biographical Sources for Archbishops of Canterbury from 1066
  to the Present day
  www.lambethpalacelibrary.org
  Click 'Research Guides' and title
- Suffolk Committees for Scandalous Ministers 1644-1646
  content.ancestry.co.uk/iexec/?htx=BookList&dbid=7519
  Subscription required

- Index of Methodist Ministers
  www.library.manchester.ac.uk/specialcollections/collections/
                              methodist/using/indexofministers/
- American Emigrant Ministers 1690-1811
  www.ancestry.com/search/db.aspx?dbid=4760
  Subscription required

Clock & Watchmakers
- The Horological Wiki
  www.clockmakers.archivist.info/
  Lists clock and watchmakers
- Historical Clock & Watch Research: British & Irish Makers
  Research Archives
  www.clockswatches.com
- British Horological Institute
  www.bhi.co.uk
  Includes list of clockmakers' obituaries, a list of 'clock dating
  reference books', *etc.*

Coal Miners
- Coal Mining History Resource Centre
  www.cmhrc.pwp.blueyonder.co.uk
  Includes a 'database of mining deaths in Great Britain'
- Coal Mining Records in the National Archives
  www.nationalarchives.gov.uk/catalogue/researchguidesindex.asp
  Click title

Durham
- Durham County Record Office: Colliery Personnel Records
  www.durham.gov.uk/recordoffice/usp.nsf/lookup/
                              pdfhandlists/$file/subjectguide07.pdf
- Coal Industry
  www.tyneandweararchives.org.uk/pdf/userguide9a.pdf
  Records held by Tyne & Wear Archives Service

Coastguards
- Coastguard
  www.nationalarchives.gov.uk/catalogue/researchguidesindex.asp
  Click title

- British Coastguard Records
  www.mariners-l.co.uk/UKCoastguards.html
- British Coastguards 1841-1891
  www.genuki.org.uk/big/Coastguards

Conscientious Objectors
- First World War Conscientious Objectors & exemptions from service
  www.nationalarchives.gov.uk/catalogue/researchguidesindex.asp
  Click title

Convicts, Criminals, Prisoners, *etc. see also* Hangmen
- Convicts and Prisoners, 1100-1986
  www.nationalarchives.gov.uk/catalogue/researchguidesindex.asp
  Click title
- Sources for the History of Crime and the Law in England
  www.nationalarchives.gov.uk/nra/guides/
  Click title. Noted in the National Register of Archives
- Genealogy Quest: Special Collection: Crime and Punishment
  www.genealogy-quest.com/Crime__and__Punishment/
  Many pages of transcribed original sources, especially criminal pardons 1770-75, and transported convicts
- Ancestors and the Law: Criminal Courts
  www.nationalarchives.gov.uk/familyhistory/guide/
  ancestorslaw/default.htm
- Tracing 19th Century Criminals in the National Archives
  www.nationalarchives.gov.uk/catalogue/researchguidesindex.asp
  Click title
- Black (and white) Sheep index
  www.lightage.demon.co.uk/BSINOTES.htm
  Index of 200,000 villains, 1860-1900
- List of Executions: England 1606 onwards
  www.fred.net/jefalvey/execute.html
- Capital Punishment in the United Kingdom
  www.murderfile.net/index2.htm
  List of executed criminals, 20th c.
- Victorian Prisoners Photograph Albums
  www.nationalarchives.gov.uk/documentsonline/
  Browse categories: Family History, and click title

Bedfordshire
- 19th Century Bedford Gaol 1801-77
  www.schools.bedfordshire.gov.uk/gaol/intro.htm
  Index of prisoners

Buckinghamshire
- Victorian Prisoners: Aylesbury Gaol in the 19th Century
  www.buckscc.gov.uk/bucks__prisoners
  Database of prisoners admitted in the 1870's

Derbyshire
- Crime in Derbyshire 1770-1828
  www.wirksworth.org.uk/CRIME.htm
  Index of 8777 cases from Derbyshire Quarter Sessions and Petty Sessions

Hertfordshire
- Hertfordshire Transportees
  www.hertsfhs.org.uk/hfphs38.html

Kent
- A Summary of the Records of Maidstone Gaol
  freepages.genealogy.rootsweb.com/~mrawson/gaolrec.html
  Names of prisoners, 1728-1833

Lancashire
- Walton Gaol H.M.Prison, Walton-on-the-Hill, Lancashire, England: List of Staff and Prisoners, 1881
  www.rootsweb.com/~engchs/WAL.html
  List of staff and prisoners

Lincolnshire
- Lincolnshire Convicts Transported to Australia, Gibraltar and Bermuda
  www.lincolnshire.gov.uk/archives/section.asp?docId=27638

London & Middlesex
- Convicts Transported from Middlesex
  www.cityoflondon.gov.uk/Corporation/leisure__heritage/
  libraries__archives__museums__galleries/lma/
  visitor__information/free__information__leaflets.htm
  Click title

- Newgate Prison: a List of Inmates, Victims, and those associated with the Prison
  www.fred.net/jefalvey/newgate.html
- The complete Newgate Calendar
  tarlton.law.utexas.edu/lpop/etext/completenewgate.htm
- Newgate Calendar
  www.exclassics.com/newgate/ngintro.htm

Somerset
- Ilchester Gaol Registers
  www.somerset.gov.uk/archives/database/Prisoner.htm

Staffordshire
- Staffordshire Calendar of Prisoners
  www.uk-transcriptions.accessgenealogy.com/
  Staffs%20Prisoners%20Intro.htm
  Excel file

Warwickshire
- Warwickshire County Record Office Calendars of Prisoners Database
  www.warwickshire.gov.uk/countyrecordoffice
  Click 'Online catalogues & databases', and title
- Coventry Family History Society: Convicts Register 1879, 1890-1897
  www.covfhs.org
  Click 'databases'

Yorkshire
- An Index to Records held in York Reference Library of Prisoners brought to trial at York Assizes, 1785-1851
  www.yorkfamilyhistory.org.uk/assizes.htm

OVERSEAS
- Prisoners and Transportation
  www.familyhistory.gov.uk/familyhistory/guide/ancestorslaw/
  prisoners.htm
- Transportation and Emigration
  www.cityoflondon.gov.uk/Corporation/leisure__heritage/
  libraries__archives__museums__galleries/lma/
  visitor__information/free__information__leaflets.htm

Australia
- Convicts to Australia: a guide to researching your convict ancestors
  www.convictcentral.com
- Convicts Australia
  www.hotkey.net.au/~jwilliams4/cons.htm
  Links page
- Convict Arrivals in New South Wales (NSW) 1788-1842
  www.familyhistoryonline.net/database/GSVConvicts.shtml
  Pay per view
- First Fleet
  cedir.uow.edu.au/programs/FirstFleet/
  Includes database of 780 convicts who sailed to Australia in 1787
- Transportation to Australia 1787-1868
  www.nationalarchives.gov.uk/catalogue/researchguidesindex.asp
  Click title
- Claim-a-Convict: Convicts to Australia
  users.bigpond.net.au/convicts/
  Includes a database of convicts

North America
- Transportation to America and the West Indies 1615-1776
  www.nationalarchives.gov.uk/catalogue/researchguidesindex.asp
  Click title

Cricketers
- Cricket Archive
  www.cricketarchive.co.uk/
  Includes details of 127,000+ players
- Cricinfo Players
  content-uk.cricinfo.com/ci/content/player/
  Lists international cricketers
- The Association of Cricket Statisticians & Historians
  acscricket.com

Customs and Excise Officers
- British Customs and Excise Men
  www.mariners-l.co.uk/UKCustoms.html
- Customs Officers and Excise Men
  www.nationalarchives.gov.uk/familyhistory/guide/trade/
  customs.htm

- Customs and Excise Officials and Tax Collectors
  www.nationalarchives.gov.uk/researchguidesindex.asp
  Click title
- Customs Records as a Source for Genealogical Research
  www.hmrc.gov.uk
  Search 'genealogical' and click title. Brief note on staff records
- Tracing Your Ancestors who were in the H.M. Customs and Excise Department
  www.liverpoolmuseums.org.uk/maritime/archive/
  displayGuide.aspx?sid=48

Cyclists
- Sources for the History of Cycling
  www2.warwick.ac.uk/services/library/mrc/subject__guides/
  ncyaleaflet2.pdf

Dentists
- Dental Surgeons Directory 1925
  www.findmypast.com/Directories.jsp
  Click title. Pay per view

Divers
- The Divers Index
  www.thehds.com/divers/
  The index itself is not online

Dockyard Workers
- Royal Naval Dockyards
  www.nationalarchives.gov.uk/catalogue/
  researchguidesindex.asp
  Click title. Records of dockyard employees

Doctors *see* Medical Men

Drovers
- Welsh Cattle Drovers in the Nineteenth Century
  www.genuki.org.uk/big/wal/CattleDrovers1.html

East Indiamen
- Search Migration 1793-1960
  www.findmypast.com/Migration.jsp
  Includes various Indian Army and Civil Service lists. Pay per view

Electrical Engineers
- The Institution of Electrical Engineers (IEE) Archives
  archives.iee.org/

Entertainers & Broadcasters
- Sources for the History of Film, Television and the Performing Arts
  www.nationalarchives.gov.uk/nra/guides/
  Click title. Listed in the National Register of Archives

Fishermen
- Tracing details of Fishermen
  www.angelfire.com/de/BobSanders/FISHER.html

Footballers
- England Football Online
  www.englandfootballonline.com/TeamPlyrs/AppsRecent.html
  List of England players
- Association of Football Statisticians
  www.11v11.co.uk/
  Database of 46,000 players

Foundlings
- Finding your Foundling
  www.cityoflondon.gov.uk/Corporation/leisure__heritage/
  libraries__archives__museums__galleries/lma/
  visitors__information/free__information__leaflets.htm
  Click title
- The Foundling Museum
  www.foundlingmuseum.org.uk
  Includes 'Trace your Foundling' page

Freemasons
- Centre for Research into Freemasonry
  freemasonry.dept.shef.ac.uk/

Gardeners & Horticulturalists
- Sources for Garden History
  www.nationalarchives.gov.uk/nra/guides/
  Click title. In the National Register of Archives

- Records of Gardening and Horticulture
  www.cityoflondon.gov.uk/Corporation/leisure__heritage/
  libraries__archives__museums__galleries/lma/
  visitor__information/free__information__leaflets.htm
  Click title. In London Metropolitan Archives

Gas Men
- The National Gas Archive
  www.gasarchive.org

Gun Makers
- Historical Database of Gun Makers
  www.internetgunclub.com/general/history.php
- Stan Cook's Gunmakers & Allied Trades Index
  www.genuki.org.uk/big/Gunmakers.html

Gypsies
- Gypsy Lore Society Collections
  sca.lib.liv.ac.uk/collections/colldescs/gls.html
- Gypsy Index
  www.leics.gov.uk/index/community/museums/record__office/
  record__office__gypsy__index.htm

Hackney Coachmen
- A list of the 400 Hackney-coaches licensed in July and August
  1662 ...
  freepages.history.rootsweb.com/~frpayments/HC1662/
  In London

Hangmen
- Capital Punishment U.K.
  www.richard.clark32.btinternet.co.uk
  Includes list of public executions, 1828-36; biographical notes on
  hangmen, 1850-1964, *etc.*

Hemp & Flax Growers
- Hemp and Flax Growers Index
  www.familyhistoryonline.net/database/
  SomersetDorsetFHSgrowers.shtml
  Pay per view. Record of bounties paid to growers in Dorset 1783-91

Heralds
- Heralds of England, Scotland and Ireland
  www.heraldica.org/topics/britain/heralds.htm
  List

Highwaymen *see* Outlaws

Horse Racing Fraternity
- Horse Racing History Online
  www.horseracinghistory.co.uk
  Click 'browse archive' for brief biographies of trainers, jockeys,
  owners and breeders

Innkeepers
- Pub History Society
  www.pubhistory.freeserve.co.uk/
- Pub History Society leaflet 1: Tracing Ancestors who Worked in
  Pubs
  www.sfowler.force9.co.uk/page__27.htm
- Pub History
  www.sfowler.force9.co.uk/page__12.htm
- 1881 Pubs: a Directory of English Pubs in the 1881 Census
  www.1881pubs.com
- Midlands Pubs
  www.midlandspubs.co.uk
  Includes a 'genealogy forum'

Bedfordshire
- Bedfordshire: Victuallers Licences
  www.genuki.org.uk/big/eng/BDF/VictuallerLicences/
  Lists records available

Buckinghamshire
- Public Houses in Buckinghamshire: a short guide to sources
  www.buckscc.gov.uk/bcc/content/
  index.jsp?contentid=1505873348

Cambridgeshire
- Cambridgeshire: Victuallers' Licences
  www.genuki.org.uk/big/eng/CAM/VictuallerLicences.html
  Lists records available

- 1839 Pigot's Directory of Cambridgeshire: Index of Inns & Hotels, Taverns and Public Houses, Brewers & Maltsters, Wine & Spirit Merchants
  freepages.genealogy.rootsweb.com/%7Ecawthorn/1839Pigots/ 1839index.html

Cornwall
- West Penwith Resources: Public Houses (1), including inns, taverns and hotels
  www.west-penwith.org.uk/wpeninn.htm

Essex *see* London & Middlesex

Gloucestershire
- Gloucestershire Pubs
  www.easywell.co.uk/pubs/
  Includes list of pubs and licencees

Hampshire
- Alehouse Licences between 1766-1819
  www.iwight.com/library/record_office/alehouses
  Database for the Isle of Wight

London & Middlesex
- Licensed Victuallers Records
  www.cityoflondon.gov.uk/Corporation/leisure_heritage/ libraries_archives_museums_galleries/lma/ visitor_information/free_information_leaflets.htm
  Click title. Including list of records in London Metropolitan Archives

Norfolk
- Norfolk Public Houses
  www.norfolkpubs.co.uk
  Traces licencees *etc.*

Shropshire
- Shropshire Family History Society: Inns of 1828
  www.sfhs.org.uk/Inns1828.asp
  Lists innkeepers

Wales
- Welsh Historic Inns
  www.welsh-historic-inns.com/pub_history.php
  Guide to tracing innkeepers

Caernarvonshire
- Alehouse Recognizances 1764-1824
  www.rootsweb.com/~wlsccaer/recog.html
  Database for Caernarvonshire

Internees
- Internees: First and Second World Wars
  www.nationalarchives.gov.uk/catalogue/researchguidesindex.asp
  Click title

Jockeys *see* Horse Racing Fraternity

Journalists & Newspapermen
- Sources for the History of the Press
  www.nationalarchives.gov.uk/nra/guides
  Click title. Listed in the National Register of Archives

Land Tax Commissioners
- An Act to Appoint Additional Commissioners for ... a land tax ... 1866
  www.londonancestor.com/comm/comm-menu.htm
  Includes list of land tax commissioners 1866, for the whole country

Lawyers *see also* Attorneys
- Lawyers: Records of Attornies and Solicitors
  www.nationalarchives.gov.uk/catalogue/researchguidesindex.asp
  Click title
- How to Trace a Past Solicitor
  www.lawsociety.org.uk/productsandservices/libraryservices/ legalresearchguides
  Click title
- The Law List 1843
  content.ancestry.com/iexec/?htx=List&dbid=8022
  Subscription required

- The Inner Temple Admissions Database
  www.innertemple.org.uk/archive/itad/index.asp
  Admissions 1547-1850

Leather Workers
- Walsall Leather Museum
  www.walsall.gov.uk/leathermuseum

Lighthouse Keepers
- Sources for Lighthouse History
  www.history.ac.uk/gh/lhouse.htm
- Lighthouse Personnel in England, Wales and the Channel Islands
  c.1790-1911
  www.genuki.org.uk/big/Lighthouses/

Liverymen
- Sources for tracing apprenticeship and membership in City livery
  companies and related organisations
  www.history.ac.uk/gh/livdet.html
- Searching for Members or those Apprenticed to Members of City
  of London Livery Companies
  www.history.ac.uk/gh/livapp.htm
- Livery Company Membership Guide
  www.history.ac.uk/gh/livintro.htm
  Includes list of sources by Company

Lunatics
- Lunatic Asylums, 18-20th Centuries
  www.nationalarchives.gov.uk/catalogue/researchguidesindex.asp
  Click title
- Lunacy and the State
  www.nationalarchives.gov.uk/catalogue/researchguidesindex.asp
  Click title

Mathematicians
- The Davis Archive: Mathematical Women in the British Isles
  1878-1940
  www-history.mcs.st-andrews.ac.uk/Davis/index.html
  Database listing all female mathematics graduates

Medical Men *see also* Nurses
- Hospital Records Database
  www.nationalarchives.gov.uk/hospitalrecords/
  National listing, including staff and patient records, although the
  latter are usually closed for 100 years
- Medical Archives and Manuscripts Survey
  library.wellcome.ac.uk/node265.html
- Sources for Tracing Apothecaries, Surgeons, Physicians and other
  medical practitioners at Guildhall Library
  www.history.ac.uk/gh/apoths.htm
- Was Your Ancestor a Doctor?
  user.itl.net/~glen/doctors.html
  Many links
- Directory of Medical Licences issued by the Archbishop of
  Canterbury 1535-1775
  www.lambethpalacelibrary.org/holdings/Catalogues/medics/
  medics__intro.html
- Physicians and Irregular Medical Practitioners in London
  1550-1640: Database
  www.british-history.ac.uk/source.asp?pubid=107
- Royal College of Physicians: Heritage Centre
  www.rcplondon.ac.uk/heritage/
- Medical Register 1913
  www.findmypast.com/Directories.jsp
  Click title. Pay per view

Members of Parliament
- The History of Parliament
  www.histparl.ac.uk/
  Description of the authoritative biographical dictionary of
  Members of Parliament

Merchant Taylors
- The Membership Records of the Merchant Taylors Company
  www.history.ac.uk/gh/merchmem.htm

Merchants
- Mercantile Liverpool Project
  www.liv.ac.uk/merchant/
  Database of Liverpool merchants

Miners *see also* Coal Miners
- Sources for the History of Mines and Quarries
  www.nationalarchives.gov.uk/catalogue/researchguidesindex.asp
  Click 'Mines & Quarries'
- British Mining Database
  shropshiremines.org.uk/bmd/index.htm
- Mines and Quarries
  www.lightage.demon.co.uk/MINING.htm
  Lists miners who died in accidents and disasters. Reports must be purchased
- National Mining Memorabilia Association
  www.mining-memorabilia.co.uk/
  The links page is a gateway to many sites related to mines and miners

Cornwall
- Cornish Mining Index
  www.cornwall-online.co.uk/jumppage-cmi.htm
  Subscription required

Durham
- Durham Mining Museum
  www.dmm.org.uk
  Includes lists of victims in mining disasters, also notes for family historians

Missionaries
- Mundus: Gateway to Missionary Collections in the United Kingdom
  www.mundus.ac.uk
- Centre for Baptist History and Heritage
  www.rpc.ox.ac.uk/cbhh/Centre.htm
  Includes details of the Angus Library, including Baptist Missionary Society archives
- C.M.S. Archives
  www.cms-uk.org/CrowtherCentre/Archives/tabid/194/
  Default.aspx

Municipal Officers
Chester
- Chester's Mayors and Sheriffs 1238-2007
  www.chester.gov.uk/council__and__democracy/
  city__councillors/lord__mayor__and-civic__functions/
  mayors__and__sheriffs.aspx

London
- The Rulers of London 1660-1689: a biographical record of the Aldermen and Common Council men of the City of London
  www.british-history.ac.uk/source.asp?pubid=7
  From a book published in 1966
- Cripplegate Ward, London: Aldermen 1276-1900
  content.ancestry.co.uk/iexec/?htx=List&dbid=8488
  Subscription required

Nurses
- Royal College of Nursing: Historical Nursing Archives
  www.rcn.org.uk/resources/historyofnursing
- United Kingdom Centre for the History of Nursing & Midwifery
  www.ukchnm.org/
- Angels and Orderlies
  www.dorsetbay.plus.com/source/nurselist.htm
  Lists Crimean War nurses
- Civilian Nurses and Nursing Services
  www.nationalarchives.gov.uk/catalogue/researchguidesindex.asp
  Click title
- British Army: Nurses and Nursing Services
  www.nationalarchives.gov.uk/catalogue/researchguidesindex.asp
  Click title
- Royal Air Force: Nurses and Nursing Services
  www.nationalarchives.gov.uk/catalogue/researchguidesindex.asp
  Click title
- Royal Navy: Nurses and Nursing Services
  www.nationalarchives.gov.uk/catalogue/researchguidesindex.asp
  Click title
- Women in Uniform
  www.familyrecords.gov.uk/focuson/womeninuniform
  Includes pages on nurses in the Crimean War and in the British Army, the Womens Royal Naval Service, and women in World War II

- History of Nursing: major sources in the London Metropolitan Archives
  www.cityoflondon.gov.uk/leisure__heritage/
  libraries_archives_museums_galleries/lma/
  visitor__information/free__information__leaflets.htm
  Click title
- Volunteers and Personnel Records
  www.redcross.org.uk/standard.asp?id=3423
  VAD nurses, World War I
- Voluntary Aid Detachments in the First World War
  collections.iwm.org.uk/upload/pdf/Info40.pdf
- British Voluntary Aid Detachments in the Second World War
  collections.iwm.org.uk/upload/pdf/Bk362/pdf

Outlaws
- Outlawry in Medieval and Early Modern England
  www.nationalarchives.gov.uk/catalogue/researchguidesindex.asp
  Click title
- Outlaws and Highwaymen: the history of the Highwaymen and their predecessors, the medieval outlaw
  www.outlawsandhighwaymen.com
- Stand and Deliver! Records of Highwaymen and Horse Thieves
  www.bedfordshire.gov.uk/CommunityAndLiving/
  ArchivesAndRecordOffice/NeslettersandArticles/
  HighwaymenHorseThieves.aspx
  In Bedfordshire

Papermakers
- British Association of Paper Historians
  www.baph.org.uk
- Papermakers in ...
  www.papermakers.org.uk/
  Extracts from 1881 census: for Berkshire, Hampshire, and Oxfordshire only to date
- The papermakers of Snodland c.1740-1854
  www.kentarchaeology.ac/authors/003.pdf
  Brief biographies
- Paper-Mills and Paper-Makers in Wales 1700-1900
  www.genuki.org.uk/big/wal/Paper.html

Parish Clerks
- The Parish Clerk Index
  steve.pickthall.users.btopenworld.com/pci/
  Lists parish clerks by county

Patients *see also* Medical Men

London & Middlesex
- Records of Patients in London Hospitals
  www.cityoflondon.gov.uk/Corporation/leisure__heritage/
  libraries_archives_museums_galleries/lma/
  visitor__information/free-information__leaflets.htm
  Click title

Wiltshire
- Salisbury Infirmary Admissions and Discharges
  www.familyhistoryonline.net/database/WiltsFHSHospital.shtml
  Pay per view

Photographers
- Early Photographers
  www.thornburypump.myby.co.uk
- Victorian Photographers of Britain 1855-1901
  mywebpage.netscape.com/hibchris/instant/aboutme.html
- Royal Photographic Society Historical Group
  www.rps.org/groups__detail.php?ID=8
- Directory of London Photographers 1841-1908
  www.photolondon.org.uk/directory.htm
- Liverpool Photographers
  freepages.genealogy.rootsweb.com/~liverpoolphotographers
  Lists from numerous directories

Physicians *see* Medical Men

Pilots
- Bristol Channel Pilots
  hometown.aol.com/PRode18115/
- Liverpool Pilots
  www.liverpoolmuseums.org.uk/maritime/archive/
  displayGuide.aspx?sid=68

- Thames Pilot
  www.thamespilot.org.uk

Police
- Police History Society
  www.policehistorysociety.co.uk
- Police Index
  www.lightage.demon.co.uk/POLNOTES.htm
  70,000 entries, 1860-1920. Reports must be purchased
- National Police Officers Roll of Honour
  www.policememorial.org.uk
  Lists 4000 officers who lost their lives whilst on duty
- Transport Police
  www.nationalarchives.gov.uk/catalogue/researchguidesindex.asp
  Click title
- British Transport Police
  www.btp.police.uk
  Click 'History of BTP' for pages on 'family history enquiries', 'roll of honour', *etc.*

Bedfordshire
- Records of the Bedfordshire Police
  www.bedfordshire.gov.uk/CommunityAndLiving/
                                        ArchivesAndRecordOffice/
  Click 'Guide to collections' and title

Buckinghamshire
- Newport Pagnell Police Museum
  www.mkheritage.co.uk/nppm/index.html

London & Middlesex
- History of the Metropolitan Police
  www.met.police.uk/history/
  Includes book of remembrance
- Historical Records of the Metropolitan Police Service
  www.met.police.uk/information/historical_enquiries.htm
- Metropolitan Police (London): Records of Service
  www.nationalarchives.gov.uk/catalogue/researchguidesindex.asp
  Click title (under 'Police')

Staffordshire
- Staffordshire Police Index
  www.staffordshire.gov.uk/leisure/archives/OnlineCatalogues/
                                        StaffordshirePoliceIndex.htm
  Index to personnel records, 1842-94

Glamorganshire
- Glamorgan Record Office: Police Records
  www.glamro.gov.uk/adobe/police1.pdf

Postmen
- The British Postal Museum & Archive
  www.postalheritage.org.uk

Potters
- A to Z of Stoke on Trent Potters
  www.thepotteries.org/allpotters/index.htm

Prison Officers
- Prisons
  www.institutions.org.uk/prisons/
  Gazetteer with names of some officers and notes on records

Prisoners of War
- Tracing Prisoners of War
  www.iwm.org.uk/upload/pdf/famhist_pow2007.pdf
- British Prisoners of War c.1760-1919
  www.nationalarchives.gov.uk/catalogue/researchguidesindex.asp
  Click title
- Prisoners of War (British) 1939-1953
  www.nationalarchives.gov.uk/catalogue/researchguidesindex.asp
  Click title
- British Prisoners of War: Interviews and Reports
  www.nationalarchives.gov.uk/documentsonline/pow.asp
  World War I; 3000 names. Pay per view database
- PoW Research Network Japan
  homepage3.nifty.com/pow-j/e
- The Changi Museum: Civilian Internees Database
  www.changimuseum.com/search_engine/search_index.htm

Psychiatrists & Psychologists
- Sources Leaflets: Psychiatry, Psychology, Psychoanalysis: (1) Personal Papers
  library.wellcome.ac.uk/doc_WTL039940.html

Quarrymen
- Stone & Quarrymen of the West Country: a genealogical index of stone workers and related occupations in Cornwall and Devon
  freepages.genealogy.rootsweb.com/~stonemen

Railwaymen
- Railways: Staff Records
  www.nationalarchives.gov.uk/catalogue/researchguidesindex.asp
  Click title
- National Railway Museum
  www.nrm.org.uk/
  Includes page on 'railway staff records'
- Railway Index
  www.lightage.demon.co.uk/RAILWAY.htm
  Index to personal injury reports of rail disaster enquiries. Reports must be purchased
- Railways Staff Register
  www.cheshire.gov.uk/Recordoffice/Railways/Home.htm
  Index to c.25,000 railwaymen from North-West England, c.1869-1950
- Tracking Railway Archives Project
  www.trap.org.uk
  Includes database of railway archives in small repositories
- L.N.E.R. Magazine vol.29 no.5. May 1939
  www.btinternet.com/~nttsue/LNERmagazine.html
  Includes many names of railway staff
- London and North Western Railway Society
  www.lnwrs.org.uk/
  Click 'staff history' for various databases, *etc.*
- Staff Records of the GWR: God's Wonderful Railway
  www.berksfhs.org.uk/journal/Sep2003
  General discussion
- England: *Great Western Railway Magazine,* 1838-1943
  www.ancestry.com/search/db.aspx?dbid=4953

- The Midland Railway Study Centre
  www.midlandrailwaystudycentre.org.uk

Refugees
- Refugees and Minorities
  www.nationalarchives.gov.uk/catalogue/researchguidesindex.asp
  Click title

Royal Household Officers & Servants *see also* Royal Warrant Holders
- The Database of Court Officers 1660-1837
  www.luc.edu/history/fac_resources/bucholz/DCO/DCO.html

Royal Marines
- Family History: Royal Marines
  www.nationalarchives.gov.uk/familyhistory/military/marines/
- Royal Marines: Officers Service Records
  www.nationalarchives.gov.uk/catalogue/researchguidesindex.asp
  Click title
- Royal Marines: Other Ranks Service Records
  www.nationalarchives.gov.uk/catalogue/researchguidesindex.asp
  Click title
- Royal Marines: How to Find a Division
  www.nationalarchives.gov.uk/catalogue/researchguidesindex.asp
  Click title
- Royal Marines: Further Areas of Research
  www.nationalarchives.gov.uk/catalogue/researchguidesindex.asp
  Click title

Royal Warrant Holders
- Royal Warrant Holders and Suppliers of Goods, from 1660
  www.nationalarchives.gov.uk/catalogue/researchguidesindex.asp
  Click title
- Royal Warrant Holders and Household Servants
  www.nationalarchives.gov.uk/catalogue/researchguidesindex.asp
  Click title

Scriveners
- Scriveners Company Common Paper 1357-1628
  www.british-history.ac.uk/source.asp?pubid=152
  From a London Record Society publication, 1968. Many names of apprentices, members, officers, *etc.*

Seamen (Merchant Navy) *see also* Boatmen, & Watermen & Lightermen

General
- British Mercantile Records of the 19th and 20th centuries
  www.barnettresearch.freeserve.co.uk/main.htm
- Sources for Maritime History
  www.nationalarchives.gov.uk/catalogue/researchguidesindex.asp
  Click title
- Sources for Maritime History
  www.nationalarchives.gov.uk/nra/guides/
  Click title. Listed in the National Register of Archives.
- Mariners Research Links
  www.angelfire.com/de/BobSanders/Site.html
  Many pages of guidance on tracing British seamen and their ships.
- Mariners: United Kingdom
  www.mariners-l.co.uk/UKPages.htm
  Many useful pages for both the Royal Navy and merchant seamen, *etc.*
- Merchant Navy
  www.nationalarchives.gov.uk/familyhistory/merchant/
- Merchant Seamen of Britain and its former colonies
  homepages.tesco.net/~ct__watts/merchsea.htm
- Tracing Seafaring Ancestors in the Merchant Navy
  www.liverpoolmuseums.org.uk/maritime/archive/
  displayGuide.aspx?sid=47
- Tracing Family History from Maritime Records
  www.nmm.ac.uk/server/show/conWebDoc.2594
- Tracing Merchant Navy apprentices
  www.angelfire.com/de/Bob Sanders/MNAPPS.html
- Tracing Merchant Navy Ancestry
  www.iwm.org.uk/upload/pdf/famhist-merchant2006.pdf
- Tracing Seafaring Ancestors in the Merchant Navy
  www.liverpoolmuseums.org.uk/maritime/archive/
  displayGuide.aspx?sid=47
- United Kingdom and Ireland Merchant Marine
  www.genuki.org.uk/big/MerchantMarine.html
  Links to a variety of sites

Particular Sources
- Crew List Index Project
  www.crewlist.org.uk
  Index, 1861-1913
- Merchant Seamen: Records of the RGSS: A guide to leaflets
  www.nationalarchives.gov.uk/catalogue/researchguidesindex.asp
  Click title
- Merchant Seamen: Crew Lists and Agreements, 1747-1860
  www.nationalarchives.gov.uk/catalogue/researchguidesindex.asp
  Click title
- Merchant Seamen: Crew Lists and Agreements after 1861
  www.nationalarchives.gov.uk/catalogue/researchguidesindex.asp
  Click title
- Merchant Seamen: Interpreting the Voyages in the Registers of Seamens Tickets and the Alphabetical Registers of Masters
  www.nationalarchives.gov.uk/catalogue/researchguidesindex.asp
  Click title
- Merchant Seamen: Interpreting Voyage Seamen's petitions for pensions *etc.* Pay per view. Details in the Registers of Seamen, series II
  www.nationalarchives.gov.uk/catalogue/researchguidesindex.asp
  Click title
- Records of the Corporation of Trinity House at Guildhall Library
  www.history.ac.uk/gh/thouse.htm
  The Corporation had charge of lighthouses throughout England, and of pilotage in London and its (many) outports; it was also a charity for distressed mariners. See also /thouse2.htm
- Trinity House Calendars 1787-1854
  www.originsnetwork.com/help/popup-aboutbo-trinity2.htm
  Pay per view
- Lloyds Captains Registers at Guildhall Library and related sources
  www.history.ac.uk/gh/capreg.htm
- Indexes to Lloyds Captains Registers
  www.history.ac.uk/gh/capintro.htm
- Lloyds Register: Marine Shipping Information: Information Sheets
  www.lr.org/Industries/Marine/Services/Shipping+information/
  Information+sheets.htm
  Includes various historical leaflets, including one on 'Genealogists sources'

Archives & Museums

- Merseyside Maritime Museum
  www.liverpoolmuseums.org.uk/maritime/
  Includes details of an important archive for tracing merchant seamen, emigrants, *etc.* Many useful information leaflets.
- National Maritime Museum
  www.nmm.ac.uk
- Maritime History Archive
  www.mun.ca/mha/
  At the Memorial University of Newfoundland; holds crew lists

Merchant Seamen in World Wars I & II

- Merchant Seamen: Medals and Honours
  www.nationalarchives.gov.uk/catalogue/researchguidesindex.asp
  Click title
- Researching Seafaring Ancestors in World War One
  www.liverpoolmuseums.org.uk/maritime/archive/
  displayGuide.aspx?sid=17
- Merchant Seaman Medals
  www.liverpoolmuseums.org.uk/maritime/archive/
  displayGuide.aspx?sid=14
- World War Two Medals issued to Merchant Seamen
  www.nationalarchives.gov.uk/documentsonline/
  seamens-medals.asp
  Pay per view

Regional

- Through Mighty Seas: merchant sailing ships of the N.W. of England
  www.mightyseas.co.uk
  Many names of captains *etc.*

Devon

- Sources for Maritime History
  www.devon.gov.uk/contrast/index/democracycommunities/
  neighbourhoods-villages/record_office/north_record_office/
  leaflets/sources_for_maritime_history.htm
  In North Devon

Kent

- Kentish Men: the Maritime Past of the Isle of Thanet
  www.beavis.co.uk/ramvess.htm
  Includes list of 'Ramsgate registered vessels 1835-1844', including names of masters

Somerset

- Bridgwater Crew List
  www.somerset.gov.uk/archives/
  Click 'search catalogues and index', and on title. c.35,000 seamen listed.

Channel Islands

- Channel Islands Maritime Miscellany
  history.foote_family.com/maritime/
  Includes Guernsey crew lists, list of 'letters of marque', i.e.privateers, *etc.*

Wales

- Welsh Mariners
  www.welshmariners.org.uk
  Index of 22,000 names

Glamorganshire

- Maritime Heritage: sources available at West Glamorgan Archive Service
  www.swansea.gov.uk/westglamorganarchives/
  index.cfm?articleid=10364
  Includes pages on 'Using maritime records' and 'crew agreements'
- Cardiff Mariners
  www.cardiffmariners.org.uk
  Database
- Swansea Mariners
  www.swanseamariners.org.uk
  Database

Seamen (Royal Navy) *see also* Nurses, *and* Soldiers, Militiamen, *etc*

General

- Tracing Royal Navy Ancestry
  www.iwm.org.uk/upload/pdf/famhist_navy2007.pdf

- Tracing Your Seafaring Ancestors in the Royal Navy
  www.liverpoolmuseums.org.uk/maritime/archive/
  displayGuide.aspx?sid=69
- British Military Records part 2. The Royal Navy
  globalgenealogy.com/globalgazette/gazfd/gazfd48.htm
- The Royal Navy
  www.nationalarchives.gov.uk/familyhistory/guide/navy
- Late 18th, 19th and early 20th Century Naval and Naval Social
  History
  www.pbenyon.plus.com/Naval.html
  Includes transcripts of many original sources
- Research
  ww2modelshop.com/research.htm
  General advice on naval research, 20th c.
- Royal Naval Research from the late seventeenth to mid twentieth
  centuries: a realistic guide to what is available to those looking
  into the careers of officers and men in naval service including the
  seagoing reserves
  www.barnettresearch.freeserve.co.uk/mainaval.htm

Service & Pension Records
- Royal Navy Officers 1660-1945
  www.nationalarchives.gov.uk/documents/
  ifa__m2__royal__navy__officers__1660__1945.pdf
- Royal Navy: Officers Service Records
  www.nationalarchives.gov.uk/catalogue/researchguidesindex.asp
  Click title
- How to Obtain Royal Navy Service Records, Medals and
  Information
  www.mod.uk/contacts/rn__records.htm
  Ministry of Defence site
- Royal Navy: Officers Service Records, First World War and
  Confidential Reports 1893-1943
  www.nationalarchives.gov.uk/catalogue/researchguidesindex.asp
  Click title
- Royal Navy: Pay and Pension Records: Commissioned Officers
  www.nationalarchives.gov.uk/catalogue/researchguidesindex.asp
  Click title
- Royal Navy: Pension Records: Ratings
  www.nationalarchives.gov.uk/catalogue/researchguidesindex.asp
  Click title

- Royal Navy: Pension Records: Warrant Officers
  www.nationalarchives.gov.uk/catalogue/researchguidesindex.asp
  Click title
- Royal Navy: Ratings Service Records 1667-1923
  www.nationalarchives.gov.uk/catalogue/researchguidesindex.asp
  Click title
- Royal Navy: Pension Records: Ratings
  www.nationalarchives.gov.uk/catalogue/researchguidesindex.asp
  Click title
- Naval Historical Collectors & Research Association
  www.nhcra-online.org/main.htm

Specific Periods
- Broadside
  www.nelsonsnavy.co.uk
  Life in the Royal Navy, late 18th-early 19th c.
- The Age of Nelson
  www.ageofnelson.org
  Includes details of CDs, listing commissioned officers 1793-1815,
  and those who fought at Trafalgar
- The Trafalgar Roll
  www.genuki.org.uk/big/eng/Trafalgar
  Includes names of 1640 men who served at the battle
- Trafalgar Ancestors
  www.nationalarchives.gov.uk/aboutapps/trafalgarancestors/
  Database listing c.18,000 combatants
- Royal Naval Seamen (1873-1923)
  www.nationalarchives.gov.uk/documentsonline/
  royal-navy-service.asp
  Service registers of c.500,000 seamen. Pay per view
- Naval Biographical Database: People, Places, Ships, Organisation
  and Events associated with the Royal Navy since 1660
  www.navylist.org/
- 1901 Census: Royal Navy Ships
  homepage.ntlworld.com/jeffery.naggs/RNShips.html

Specific Forces, Ships, etc
- Royal Naval Division (1914-1919)
  www.nationalarhives.gov.uk/documentsonline/
  royalnavaldivision.asp
  Digitised images of 50,000 service records; pay per view

- The Royal Naval Reserve
  www.nationalarchives.gov.uk/catalogue/researchguidesindex.asp
  Click title
- The Royal Naval Volunteer Reserve
  www.nationalarchives.gov.uk/catalogue/researchguidesindex.asp
  Click title
- Battle Cruiser Hood
  www.hmshood.com
  Includes a crew list, 1920-41, *etc.,* with a links page listing many other sites for specific ships

Servants
- A Machine Readable Index of Manservants in England and Wales in 1780
  www.data-archive.ac.uk/findingData/snDescription.asp?sn=2741
  Details of a database

Shareholders
- The Shareholders Register of the Manchester Ship Canal
  www.gmcro.co.uk/sources/share.htm

Ship Owners
- Register of Ships
  www.reach.net/~sc001198/Lloyds.htm
  Details from Lloyds register of shipping, 1764-2003, with names of owners and masters

Soldiers, Militiamen, etc.

General
- British Army
  www.nationalarchives.gov.uk/familyhistory/guide/army
- Military History: Your Guide to Resources
  www.nationalarchives.gov.uk/militaryhistory/
- Army Museums: Ancestor Research
  www.armymuseums.co.uk/ancestor.htm
- British Military Records
  www.genuki.org.uk/big/BritMilRecs.html
  Article

- British Military Records, part 1: the Army
  www.globalgenealogy.com/globalgazette/gazfd/gazfd44.htm
- British Army
  homepages.tesco.net/~ct_watts/army.htm
- England: How to Use Military Records
  www.familysearch.org
  Click 'search', 'research helps', and 'E' (for England), then scroll down to title
- Tracing Army Ancestry
  www.iwm.org/upload/pdf/famhist_army2007.pdf
- Family History using Military Sources
  www.tameside.gov.uk/familyhistory/military
  General, but including brief notes on the Manchester Regiment
- King's College London. Liddell Hart Centre for Military Archives
  www.kcl.ac.uk/iss/archives/about/lhcma.html
  Summary guide to the personal papers of hundreds of 20th century soldiers. Includes 'location register of twentieth century defence personnel'.
- Sources for the History of the Armed Forces
  www.nationalarchives.gov.uk/nra/guides/
  Click title. Listed in the National Register of Archives
- United Kingdom and Ireland Military History
  www.genuki.org.uk/big/MilitaryHistory.html
  Gateway
- United Kingdom and Ireland Military Records
  www.genuki.org.uk/big/MilitaryRecords.html
  Bibliography and links

Specific Sources
- British Army Lists
  www.nationalarchives.gov.uk/catalogue/researchguidesindex.asp
  Click title
- Army Lists
  www.armylists.org.uk/
  Includes introduction, online (pay per view) lists, and details of CDs available
- Military Records
  www.findmypast.com/MilitaryStartSearchServlet
  Armed forces births, marriages and deaths, honour rolls, and other lists. Pay per view

- British Army: Officers Commissions
  www.nationalarchives.gov.uk/catalogue/researchguidesindex.asp
  Click title
- British Courts Martial
  www.stephen-stratford.co.uk/courts_martial.htm

Nineteenth Century & Earlier
- Medieval and Early Modern Soldiers: military recruitment and service
  www.nationalarchives.gov.uk/catalogue/researchguidesindex.asp
  Click title
- British Army: Muster Rolls and Pay Lists, c.1730-1898
  www.nationalarchives.gov.uk/catalogue/researchguidesindex.asp
  Click title
- Civil War Soldiers, 1642-1660
  www.nationalarchives.gov.uk/catalogue/researchguidesindex.asp
  Click title
- British Army: Courts Martial 17th-20th centuries
  www.nationalarchives.gov.uk/catalogue/researchguidesindex.asp
  Click title
- British Army: Officers Records, 1660-1913
  www.nationalarchives.gov.uk/catalogue/researchguidesindex.asp
  Click title
- British Army Service: Officers 1757-1913
  www.nationalarchives.gov.uk/documents/
  ifa_m6_british_army_service_officers_1757_1913.pdf
- British Army: Soldiers Pensions (1702-1913)
  www.nationalarchives.gov.uk/catalogue/researchguidesindex.asp
  Click title
- British Army: Soldiers Discharge Papers 1760-1913
  www.nationalarchives.gov.uk/catalogue/researchguidesindex.asp
  Click title
- Barbara Chambers: British Army (Napoleonic Wars) and Family History Research
  members.aol.com/BJCham2909/homepage.html
- Officers Died
  www.redcoat.info/memindex3.htm
  Database of casualties in many 19th century wars

- Army Deserters (1828-1840)
  www.familyhistoryonline.net/database/
  ManLancsFHSdeserters.shtml
  Pay per view. Index of 36,578 names in the *Police gazette*

Militia & Auxiliary Forces
- Tudor and Stuart Militia Muster Rolls
  www.nationalarchives.gov.uk/catalogue/researchguidesindex.asp
  Click title
- Militia 1757-1914
  www.nationalarchives.gov.uk/catalogue/researchguidesindex.asp
  Click title
- Auxiliary Army Forces: Volunteers Yeomanry, Territorials & Home Guard 1769-1945
  www.nationalarchives.gov.uk/catalogue/researchguidesindex.asp
  Click title
- Militia Attestations Index 1886-1910
  www.originsnetwork.com/help/popup-aboutbo-militia2.htm
- Women's (later Queen Mary's Army Auxiliary Corps (1917-1920)
  www.nationalarchives.gov.uk/documentsonline/waac.asp
  Digital images of 7,000 service records. Pay per view

World War I
- British Army Officers Service Records: First World War 1914-1918
  www.nationalarchives.gov.uk/catalogue/researchguidesindex.asp
  Click title
- First World War 1914-1918: Soldiers Papers 1914-1920
  www.nationalarchives.gov.uk/catalogue/researchguidesindex.asp
  Click title
- Using the Burnt Documents at the National Archives
  www.pontefractfhs.org.uk/burnt_documents_senior.htm
- British Army WWI Pension Records 1914-1920
  content.ancestry.co.uk/iexec/?htx=List&dbid=1114
  Digitised service records. Subscription required
- First World War: Disability and Dependants Pensions
  www.nationalarchives.gov.uk/catalogues/leaflets/ri2015.htm
- Great War Index: Officers and Men of World War One
  www.lightage.demon.co.uk/GREATWARINDEX.htm

- Military - Genealogy.com
  www.military-genealogy.com
  Website of the Naval & Military Press; includes pay per view database of *Soldiers died in the Great War 1914 to 1919*, listing c.700,000 names. Also various other databases for both world wars
- Soldiers Died in the Great War 1914-1918
  www.findmypast.com
  Click 'Military' and title. Pay per view database
- National Roll of the Great War 1914-1918
  www.findmypast.com
  Click 'Military' amd title. Pay per view
- British Army: Courts Martial: First World War 1914-1918
  www.nationalarchives.gov.uk/catalogue/researchguidesindex.asp
  Click title
- The Long, Long Trail: the story of the British Army in the Great War
  www.1914-1918.net
  Includes family history guidance
- War Dead: First & Second World Wars
  www.nationalarchives.gov.uk/catalogue/researchguidesindex.asp
  Click title
- Birmingham Regimental Histories
  www.midlandhistoricaldata.org/
  SHPLoader.aspx?x=military.html
  Click title. Mainly World War I

Post World War I
- Veterans UK: Service Records
  www.veterans-uk.info/service_records/service_records.html
  Includes pages on 'service records', 'medals', 'remembrance', *etc.*
- Hong Kong War Diary
  www.hongkongwardiary.com
  Includes list of 14,000 defenders in 1941
- Army Roll of Honour 1939-1945
  www.findmypast.com
  Click 'Military' and title. Pay per view database

Medals
- Recommendations for Honours and Awards 1935-1980
  www.nationalarchives.gov.uk/documentsonline/wo373.asp
  Digitised images; pay per view

- British Armed Services: Campaign Medals and other Service Medals
  www.nationalarchives.gov.uk/catalogue/researchguidesindex.asp
  Click title
- The Victoria Cross
  www.victoriacross.org.uk/
- Victoriacross.net
  www.victoriacross.net/
- The Victoria Cross Registers
  www.nationalarchives.gov.uk/documentsonline/victoriacross.asp
  Digital images; pay per view
- Medal Rolls, World War One
  www.nationalarchives.gov.uk/militaryhistory/medals/
- World War One Medal Cards
  www.nationalarchives.gov.uk/documentsonline/medals.asp
  Pay per view site. These cards show entitlement to medals
- British Armed Services: Gallantry Medals
  www.nationalarchives.gov.uk/catalogue/researchguidesindex.asp
  Click title
- Medals, Gallantry, Armed Services: further information
  www.nationalarchives.gov.uk/catalogue/researchguidesindex.asp
  Click title
- The Western Front Association: Decorations
  www.westernfront.co.uk/thegreatwar/articles/
  indexbyclass.php?classification=8
  Pages on various different medals

Solicitors *see* Attornies & Lawyers

Speakers
- Speakers of the House of Commons 1377-1832
  content.ancestry.com/iexec/?htx=List&dbid=7673
  Subscription required

Steam Engine Makers
- The Steam Engine Makers Society: an Introduction
  www.geog.port.ac.uk/lifeline/sem_db/sem_history.html
- Steam Engine Makers Database
  www.geog.port.ac.uk/lifeline/sem_db/sem_db_home.html
  Database of 19th c. trade union records

- Steam Engine Makers Database
  www.geog.port.ac.uk/lifeline/sem_db/sem_db_home.html
  Database of 19th c. trade union records

Stockbrokers
- Records of the Stock Exchange, London, at Guildhall Library
  www.history.ac.uk/gh/stockex.htm

Students
- Cambridge University Alumni 1261-1900
  www.ancestry.com/search/db.aspx?dbid=3997
  Database compiled from J.A. Venn's *Alumni Cantabrigiensis*.
  Subscription required
- Oxford Men 1880-1892
  content.ancestry.com/iexec/?htx=List&dbid=7422
  Subscription required
- Balliol College Past Members: Genealogical and Biographical
  Sources in the College Archives
  web.balliol.ac.uk/history/pastmem/index.asp
- English Speaking Students of Medicine at Continental Universities
  www.rcpe.ac.uk/library/history/English_Students/

Sugar Bakers & Refiners
- Sugar Refiners & Sugar Bakers Database
  www.mawer.clara.net/intro.html

Surgeons *see* Medical Men

Tax Collectors *see* Civil Servants, & Customs &
Excise Men

Teachers
- Education: Records of Teachers
  www.nationalarchives.gov.uk/catalogue/researchguidesindex.asp
  Click title
- British & Foreign School Society
  www.bfss.org.uk/archive/index.html
  Includes details of archives related to teacher training
- The National Society for Promoting Religious Education
  www.natsoc.org.uk/
  The society trained teachers. Click 'The Society' for pages on
  'history' and 'archives'.

- Lincolnshire Genweb Project: School teachers, Headmasters,
  Headmistresses
  www.rootsweb.com/~englin/schoolteachers.htm
  List, mainly 19th c.

Textile Workers
- The Textile System
  www.spartacus.schoolnet.co.uk/Textiles.htm

Theatrical Workers
- Backstage
  www.backstage.ac.uk
  Details of performing arts collections in the UK
- Hiss & Boo: locating Music Hall & Variety Artistes
  www.hissbo.co.uk/musichall_artistes.shtml
- Sources for the History of London Theatres and Music Halls at
  London Metropolitan Archives
  www.cityoflondon.gov.uk/Corporation/leisure_heritage/
  libraries_archives_museums_galleries/lma/
  visitor_information/free_information_leaflets.htm
  Click title
- University of Bristol Theatre Collection
  www.bris.ac.uk/theatrecollection
- The *Era* CD-Rom Project
  www.the-era.fsnet.co.uk
  Project to publish *The Era* on CD. An important source for the
  theatrical professions

Traders
- Carnarvon Traders: a listing
  www.rootsweb.com/~wlsccaer/
  From trade directories, the census, newspapers, parish records,
  etc.

Transport Workers
- Transport for London: Corporate Archives
  www.tfl.gov.uk/tfl/foi/889.aspx

Turnpike Trustees *see* Carriers

Vets

- Veterinary Records Database
  library.wellcome.ac.uk/doc__WTX023433.html

Victuallers *see* Innkeepers

War Brides

- Data Marine's War Brides
  www.warbrides.co.uk
  Database of British war brides who married soldiers of other
  nationalities and emigrated, 1939-45

Watermen & Lightermen *see also* Boatmen

- Records of the Company of Watermen and Lightermen at
  Guildhall Library
  www.ihrinfo.ac.uk/gh/water.htm
  www.history.ac.uk/gh/water.htm
- Watermen & Lightermen
  www.parishregister.com/aboutstp.html
- Doggett's Coat & Badge Race
  www.history.ac.uk/gh/doggett.htm
  Records of a charity for London watermen
- The Barge Men
  www.bargemen.co.uk/
  Bargemen, watermen, lightermen, *etc.,* of the Thames and London
  Docks
- The Thames Watermen in the Century of Revolution
  www.geocities.com/thameswatermen/

Whalers

- The Whalers Heritage Project
  www.explorenorth.com/whalers/
  Includes various lists of whalers

Witches

- Essex Witch Trials
  www.hulford.co.uk/essex.html
  Lists c.700 people accused of being witches

10. Miscellaneous Sites

Abbreviations

- Abbreviations
  www.wakefieldfhs.org.uk/A%20to%20Z.shtml
- Gendocs: Genealogical Abbreviations and Acronyms
  www.gendocs.demon.co.uk/abbr.html
- Country and County Codes: British Isles
  www.genuki.org.uk/big/Regions/Codes.html
  Often referred to as the Chapman Codes
- Abbreviations used in the Armed Forces
  www.wakefieldfhs.org.uk/military%20abbreviations.shtml

Administrative Areas *see also* Parishes

- Administrative Regions of the British Isles
  www.genuki.org.uk/big/Regions/index.html
- British Counties, Parishes, etc., for Genealogists
  homepages.nildram.co.uk/~jimella/counties.htm
  Discussion of historic counties, hundreds, parishes, unions, *etc.*
- Parish Locator for Windows
  web.onetel.net.uk/~gdlawson/parfind.htm
  Downloadable freeware
- Counties of England Wales and Scotland prior to the 1974
  Boundary changes
  www.genuki.org.uk/big/Britain.html
  Map
- Local Government changes in the United Kingdom
  www.genuki.org.uk/big/Regions/UKchanges.html

Adoption *see also* Orphans

- Adoption Search Reunion
  www.adoptionsearchreunion.org.uk
- Adoption: England and Wales
  www.familyrecords.gov.uk/topics/adoption.htm
- General Register Office: Adoption
  www.gro.gov.uk/content/adoptions/
- Missing Links: Adoption Contact Register
  www.adoptioncontactregister.com
- UK Birth Adoption Register
  www.ukbirth-adoptionregister.com

Anglo-Indian Ancestors
- Anglo-Indians
  www.anglo-indians.com/
- Anglo-Indian Family Trees & their links to British India
  www.sumgenius.com.au/
  Collection of pedigrees
- Family History in India
  members.ozemail.com.au/~clday/
- The British in India
  www.familyrecords.gov.uk/frc/pdfs/british__in__india.pdf
- British India Family History
  valmayukuk.tripod.com/index.html
  Includes various lists of names *etc.*
- The Indiaman Magazine
  www.indiaman.com
  Magazine for the British in India

Biographical Dictionaries
- Oxford Dictionary of National Biography
  www.oup.com/oxforddnb/info
  Details of the second edition of this major reference work, which may be available online via your local public library.
- *Dictionary of National Biography*
  content.ancestry.co.uk/iexec/?htx=BookList&dbid=6892
  Subscription required. Entries from the first edition

Change of Name
- Family History: Name Changes
  www.nationalarchives.gov.uk/familyhistory/guide/ancestorslaw/name.htm
- Change of Name
  www.nationalarchives.gov.uk/catalogue/researchguidesindex.asp
  Click title

Chartists
- Chartist Ancestors
  www.chartists.net

Child Migrants *see also* Home Children
- Child Migrants Trust
  www.childmigrantstrust.com

- Child Migrant Central Information Index
  www.voluntarychild.org/
  Search 'Migrant' and click title
- Child Emigration
  www.liverpoolmuseums.org.uk/maritime/archive/displayGuide/aspx?sid=12
- Information for Former British Child Migrants
  www.dh.gov.uk/
  Search title
- Good British Stock: child and youth migration to Australia
  www.naa.gov.au/naaresources/publications/research__guides/guides/childmig/introduction.htm
- Child Migration to Australia
  www.naa.gov.au/about-us/Publications/fact__sheets/fs124.aspx
  Post-1945 records in the National Archives of Australia
- PHIND Personal History Index
  www.cberss.org/phind.html
  Index of child migrants sent to Christian Brothers homes in Australia, 1938-65

Christian Names
- Christian Names
  www.newadvent.org/cathen/10673c.htm
  Article from the *Catholic Encyclopedia*

Computers
- Genealogy Software
  www.familyrecords.gov.uk/guides/software.htm
- Software & Computers
  www.CyndisList.com/software.htm
  Links page
- Computers in Genealogy
  www.sog.org.uk/cig/cease.shtml
  Webpage of the (now defunct) journal; includes contents pages, and text of some articles
- Genealogy & Technology Articles by Mark Howells
  www.oz.net/~markhow/writing/
  Collection of articles on computing and genealogy

Contiguous Parishes

- Cambridgeshire Family History Society: Contiguous Parishes
  www.cfhs.org.uk/contiguousparishes.html
- Huntingdonshire Family History Society: Contiguous Parishes
  www.huntsfhs.org.uk/Huntingdonshire/
  ContiguousParishes.html
- Norfolk Parishes
  www.norfolkfhs.org.uk/norfolk/parishes/norfolkparishes.htm
  Includes details of contiguous parishes

Courses *see also* Events

- Institute of Local and Family History
  www.localandfamilyhistory.com
  At the University of Central Lancashire. Includes details of
  on-line courses in family history.

D.N.A.

- Cyndi's List: Genetics, D.N.A. & Family Health
  www.cyndislist.com/dna.htm
- Chris Pomery's D.N.A. Portal
  freepages.genealogy.rootsweb.com/~allpoms/genetics.html
- D.N.A. Heritage
  www.dnaheritage.com
- Geogene
  www.geogene.com
  D.N.A. testing
- Oxford Ancestors
  www.oxfordancestors.com
  D.N.A. researchers
- Sorenson Molecular Genealogy Foundation
  smgf.org

Dates & Calendars

- On-line Calendar of Saints Days
  medievalist.net/calendar/home.htm
- Chronology and Dating
  www.medievalgenealogy.org.uk/guide/chron.shtml
- Ian's English Calendar
  www.albion.edu/english/calendar/
  Includes pages on the ecclesiastical calendar, old and new style
  dating, regnal years, etc.

- Frequently Asked Questions about Calendars
  www.tondering.dk/claus/cal/
- Old Style and New Style Dates and the Change to the Gregorian
  Calendar: a summary for genealogists
  www.genfair.com/dates.htm
- Regnal Years
  www.rootsweb.com/~wlscfhs/regnalyears.pdf

Dormant Funds

- Funds in Court
  www.nationalarchives.gov.uk/catalogue/researchguidesindex.asp
  Click title

Emigrants & Emigration *see also* Child Migrants, *&* Immigrants

- Emigrants
  www.nationalarchives.gov.uk/catalogue/researchguidesindex.asp
  Click title
- Emigration
  www.familyrecords.gov.uk/topics/emigration.htm
  Brief guide for beginners
- Britons Overseas
  www.nationalarchives.gov.uk/familyhistory/guide/
  migrantancestors/overseas.htm
- United Kingdom and Ireland Emigration and Immigration
  www.genuki.org.uk/big/Emigration.html
  Links to a number of sites not listed here
- West Dorset Research Centre: Dorset Migration Local and Family History
  www.dorsetmigration.org.uk
  Includes migration database
- Virtual Jamestown: Registers of Servants Sent to Foreign
  Plantations 1654-1686
  www.virtualjamestown.org/indentures/search_indentures.html
  Searchable database of registers from Bristol, London, and
  Middlesex
- Liverpool and Emigration in the 19th and 20th Centuries
  www.liverpoolmuseums.org.uk/maritime/archive/
  displayGuide.aspx?sid=67
- Emigrants of Yorkshire: Emigration from Yorkshire & Durham:
  the Register of Emigrants
  www.eminorame.karoo.net/

- Emigration from Wales
  home.clara.net/tirbach/HelpPageemigration.html

Australia
- Emigration to Australia, New Zealand and South Africa
  www.liverpoolmuseums.org.uk/maritime/archive/
  displayGuide.aspx?sid=19
- State Records Authority of New South Wales: Indexes Online
  www.records.nsw.gov.au/archives/indexes_online_3357.asp
- Indexes to Assisted Immigrants 1839-1896
  www.records.nsw.gov.au/archives/
  assisted_immigrants_1839-96_366.asp
  Immigrants to Australia, mainly from the U.K.
- Immigrants: Making Australia Home
  www.naa.gov.uk/the_collection/family_history/
  immigrants.html
  Includes various pages on British migrants' records in the National Archives of Australia
- Immigration: State Records Authority of New South Wales
  www.records.nsw.gov.au/archives/immigration_2340.asp
- Overview of the Convict System
  www.records.nsw.gov.au/archives/convict_records_1061.asp
  In New South Wales

Canada *see also* United States
- Immigration
  www.collectionscanada.ca/genealogy/022-908-e.html
  To Canada; includes pages on passenger lists, home children, *etc.*
- Immigration of Farm Labourers to Canada 1918-1945
  www.collectionscanada.ca/archivianet/001-200.10-e.html
- Ontario Archives: Records of the Department of Immigration
  www.archives.gov.on.ca/english/interloan/i-immigration-t.htm

Malta
- Malta Family History
  maltafamilyhistory.com/
  Tracing Britons connected with the island

New Zealand *see* Australia

South Africa *see also* Australia
- British 1820 Settlers to South Africa Genealogy Web Site
  www.1820settlers.com/
- Nottinghamshire Colonists to South Africa 1820
  www.british-genealogy.com/resources/county/ntt/emigration/
  southafrica-1820/nttsa.htm

South America
- Brits in South America Database
  www.bisa.btinternet.co.uk/
- The Cornish in Latin America
  www.projects.ex.ac.uk/cornishlatin/
  Includes database of emigrants to South America
- [British Emigration to Argentina]
  www.greywall.demon.co.uk/genealogy/
- British Settlers in Argentina
  homepage.ntlworld.com/jnth/
- The British Presence in Southern Patagonia (Argentina and Chile)
  patbrit.org/
  Includes births, marriages and deaths, passenger lists, consul registrations *etc.*

United States
- Emigration to USA and Canada
  www.liverpoolmuseums.org.uk/maritime/archive/
  displayGuide.aspx?sid=20
- The Olive Tree Genealogy
  www.rootsweb.com/~ote/ships/english1773-76a.htm
  Various indexes to English emigrants to North America
- The Records of Christ's Hospital
  www.virtualjamestown.org/christs_hospital/about_ch.html
  Records of apprenticed London orphans who emigrated to North America, 17-19th c. (searchable database)
- Emigrants to North America after 1776
  www.nationalarchives.gov.uk/catalogue/
  researchguidesindex.asp
  Click title
- The Great Migration Begins: Immigrants to New England 1620-1633
  www.newenglandancestors.org/research/database/
  GreatMigrations/Default.asp
  Subscription required

- Immigrant Ancestors Project
  immigrants.byu.edu
  Database of immigrants to the U.S.A.
- A List of Emigrants from England to America, 1682-1692
  content.ancestry.com/iexec/?htx=BookList&dbid=49225
- A List of Emigrants from England to America, 1718-1759
  content.ancestry.com/iexec/?htx=BookList&dbid=49050
- Castlegarden.org: America's First Immigration Center
  castlegarden.org
  Database of 10,000,000 arrivals at Ellis Island, New York, 1830-92
- Mormon Emigration
  www.liverpoolmuseums.org.uk/maritime/archive/
  displayGuide.aspx?sid=35
- Norfolk Immigrants to Orleans County
  homepages.rootsweb.com/~djmurphy/orleans/immigrants.htm

Evacuees
- The Evacuation of Children from the County of London during the Second World War 1939-1945
  www.cityoflondon.gov.uk/Corporation/leisure__heritage/
  libraries__archives__museums__galleries/Ima/
  visitor__information/free__information__leaflets.htm
  Click title

Events
- GENEVA: an Online Calendar of GENealogical EVents and Activities
  geneva.weald.org.uk
- Society of Genealogists: Lectures, Courses, Visits and Family History Show
  www.sog.org.uk/events/calendar.shtml

Fake Titles
- Fake Titles
  www.faketitles.com/
  Don't buy one!

Funerals
- The Heraldic Funeral
  www.sealedknot.org/knowbase/docs/0103__Funeral.htm
  General discussion

Gazetteers
- England and Wales Gazetteer Entries
  www.originsnetwork.com/help/popup-aboutbo-gaz.htm
  Pay per view database of the *Comprehensive gazetteer of England and Wales* 6 vols. William Mackenzie, 1895.
- Cassells' Gazetteer of Great Britain and Ireland
  content.ancestry.co.uk/iexec/?htx=List&dbid=7305
  Subscription required
- Genuki Church Database
  www.genuki.org.uk/big/churchdb/
  Lists churches within any specified distance of the place searched
- Gazetteer of British Place Names
  www.gazetteer.co.uk
  50,000 place-names
- Genuki Gazetteer
  www.genuki.org.uk/big/Gazetteer
- United Kingdom and Ireland Parish Finder
  www.lineages.com/InfoCenter/Databases/UKParish.cfm
- UK Placename Finder
  www.digital-documents.co.uk/archi/placename.htm
- A Vision of Britain
  www.visionofbritain.org.uk
  Includes much historical information
- How to find a Present Day House, Street or Place in the UK
  www.genuki.org.uk/big/ModernLocations.html
- England Topographical Dictionary
  www.ancestry.com/search/db.aspx?dbid=3098
  Subscription required. From Lewis's *A topographical dictionary of England.* 1831.

Bedfordshire
- Guide to Bedfordshire Parishes
  www.bedfordshire.gov.uk/CommunityAndLiving/
  ArchivesAndRecordOffice/GuidesToCollections/
  GuideToBedfordshireParishes.aspx
  Historical gazetteer

Devon
- A Guide to the Manors of Devon
  www.mortimer.co.uk/manors
  Gazetteer of manors

Kent
- West Kent Parish Gazetteer
  www.nwkfhs.org.uk/parindex.htm

Lancashire
- A Select Gazetterr of Local Government Areas, Greater Manchester County
  www.gmcro.gov.uk/guides/gazette/gazframe.htm

London & Middlesex
- Victorian London A-Z street index
  www.gendocs.demon.co.uk/lon-str.html
- It all depends what you mean by 'London' …
  www.kenaud.dircon.co.uk/london.htm
  Explanation of boundaries in London

Staffordshire
- Staffordshire Online Gazetteer
  www.staffordshire.gov.uk/leisure/archives/onlinegazetteer/

Sussex
- List of Places of Worship, War Memorials, and Cemeteries in Sussex
  www.sfhg.org.uk/church.html

Yorkshire
- Alphabetical List of Places in Yorkshire
  www.genuki.org.uk/big/eng/YKS/Misc/Where/index.html

Wales
- The National Gazetteer of Wales
  homepage.ntlworld.com/geogdata/ngw/home.htm
- Wales Topographical Dictionaries 1844
  content.ancestry.com/iexec/?htx=List&dbid=8616
  Subscription required. From Lewis's *A topographical dictionary of Wales.* 1844.

Gedcom
- An Introduction to Gedcom
  www.uk-genealogy.org.uk/resources/gedcom.html

Germans
- The German Community in London
  www.cityoflondon.gov.uk/Corporation.leisure__heritage/
  libraries__archives__museums__galleries/lma/
  visitor__information/free__information__leaflets.htm
  Click title

Good Practice
- Record Offices: How to Make the Most of Their Resources
  www.ffhs.org.uk/tips/cro.php

Handwriting
- English Handwriting 1500-1700: an online course
  www.english.cam.ac.uk/ceres/ehoc/
- Palaeography: reading old handwriting 1500-1800: a practical online tutorial
  www.nationalarchives.gov.uk/palaeography/
- Deciphering Old Handwriting
  www.amberskyline.com/treasuremaps/oldhand.html
- Early English Handwriting
  www.btinternet.com/~tylcoat/handwrit.htm
- An Introduction to Palaeography
  paleo.anglo-norman.org
  From the University of Leicester; covers medieval and early modern handwriting
- Handwriting and Language
  www.medievalgenealogy.org.uk/guide/hand.shtml
- Medieval Writing: History, Heritage and Data Source
  medievalwriting.50megs.com/
- Durham Cathedral Muniments: a selection of medieval documents
  www.dur.ac.uk/medieval.documents
  Digitised images for use in a palaeographical course

Heraldry
- Heraldry on the Internet
  digiserve.com/heraldry/
- Baronage Press
  www.baronage.co.uk
  Heraldic internet newsletter

- A Display of Heraldrie, by John Guillim
  www.btinternet.com/~paul.j.grant/guillim/
  Copy of a 16th c. manual
- FOTW Heraldic Dictionary
  www.fotw.net/flags/vxt-hrld.html
- The General Armory of England, Scotland and Wales
  content.ancestry.co.uk/iexec/?htx=BookList&dbid=6326
  Subscription required
- Heraldica
  www.heraldica.org
  Includes many articles on British heraldry
- Heraldry
  www.medievalgenealogy.org.uk/guide/her.shtml
- Pimbley's Dictionary of Heraldry
  www.digiserve.com/heraldry/pimbley.htm
- The Right to Arms
  www.sog.org.uk/leaflets/arms.pdf
- Studies in Heraldry
  perso.numericable.fr/~briantimms/
- A Glossary of Terms Used in Heraldry
  www.heraldsnet.org/saitou/parker

Cheshire
- Cheshire Heraldry
  cheshire-heraldry.org.uk/portal.html
  Includes extracts from heraldic visitations

Suffolk
- Dictionary of Suffolk Arms
  content.ancestry.co.uk/iexec/?htx=List&dbid=7463
  Subscription required
- Suffolk Crests Dictionary
  content.ancestry.co.uk/iexec/?htx=List&dbid=7628
  Subscription required

Home Children
- British Home Children
  charsnow.tripod.com/one/
  Dedicated to re-uniting families
- British Home Children Society
  members.shaw.ca/persnow
  Includes registry of 50,000 children sent to Canada
- Voyages that Brought the Home Children
  www.bifhsgo.ca/home_children_voyages_1901-1904.htm
  Includes searchable database of children sent to Canada, 1872-96
- Home Children (1869-1930)
  www.collections.canada.ca/archivianet/020110_e.html
  Database of 100,000 children sent to Canada
- The British Home Children
  freepages.genealogy.rootsweb.com/~britishhomechildren
- Hidden Lives Revealed: Children in Care 1881-1918
  www.hiddenlives.org.uk
  Children's Society historical website
- Home Children
  freepages.genealogy.rootsweb.com/
  ~tweetybirdgenealogy.homechild.html
  Links page
- Passenger Lists of Home Children
  freepages.genealogy.rootsweb.com/~tweetybirdgenealogy/
  hcpasslist.html
  Collection of lists

House History
- House History: Your Guide to Resources
  www.nationalarchives.gov.uk/househistory/
- House History: a short guide to sources
  www.buckscc.gov.uk/bcc/content/
  index.jsp?contentid=1965748576
- House History
  www.wiltshire.gov.uk/wsro-house-history.htm
- The Online House Detective
  www.house-detectives.co.uk
- Researching Historic Buildings in the British Isles
  www.building-history.pwp.blueyonder.co.uk
- Tracing the History of Your House
  www.lincolnshire.gov.uk/section.asp?catId=6666
  With particular reference to Lincolnshire, but also of general interest

- Using Written Archives to Discover the History of your House
  **www.bbc.co.uk/history/familyhistory/getstarted/
  house__01.shtml**

Huguenots
- The Huguenot Society of Great Britain & Ireland
  www.huguenotsociety.org.uk/
- Huguenot Society of London Publications
  **www.cityoflondon.gov.uk/Corporation/leisure__heritage/
  libraries__archives__museums__galleries/lma/
  visitor__information/free__information__leaflets.htm**
  Click title. Vital sources for Huguenot researchers, widely
  available in libraries.

Immigrants
- Immigrants
  www.nationalarchives.gov.uk/catalogue/researchguidesindex.asp
  Click title
- Immigration and Emigration
  **www.lr.org/Industries/Marine/Services/Shipping+information/
  Information__sheets**
  Search title. Lloyds Register information sheet
- Diaspora Connections: Irish Families in Stafford 1830-1919
  cwis.livjm.ac.uk/soc/families
- Moving Here: 200 years of Migration in England
  www.movinghere.org.uk
- Every Generation: Empowering and Influencing the Black
  Community through history, family genealogy and heritage
  www.everygeneration.co.uk/

Institutions
- Rossbret Institutions Website
  www.institutions.org.uk/
  Extensive; many pages on asylums, almshouses, prisons,
  dispensaries, hospitals, reformatories, orphanages, workhouses,
  poor law, industrial schools, special school, *etc.*

Jews
- Anglo-Jewish History, 18th-20th Centuries: Sources in The National
  Archives
  www.nationalarchives.gov.uk/catalogue/researchguidesindex.asp
  Click title

- Anglo-Jewish Miscellany
  www.jeffreymaynard.com
  Various lists and indexes
- Jewish Gen: the Home of Jewish Genealogy
  www.jewishgen.org/
  Includes general information and various databases
- Jewish Genealogy: a Summary of Sources for Jewish Genealogy at
  London Metropolitan Archives and Elsewhere
  **www.cityoflondon.gov.uk/Corporation/leisure__heritage/
  libraries__archives__museums__galleries/lma/
  visitor__information/free__information__leaflets.htm**
  Click title
- The JewishCommunity in mid-19th century Britain
  www.jgsgb.org.uk/1851/Introduction.asp
  Database, mainly from the 1851 census

Journals for Genealogists, *etc. see also* Computers
- Periodical Source Index (PERSI)
  www.ancestry.co.uk/search/db.aspx?dbid=3165
  Index to U.S. journals - some of which may have articles of UK
  interest
- *Ancestors*
  www.ancestorsmagazine.co.uk
  The National Archives family history magazine's site
- *Family History Monthly*
  www.familyhistorymonthly.com
- *Family Tree Magazine* and *Practical Family History*
  www.family-tree.co.uk
  Includes details of the leading commercial journal, and a
  bookshop
- The *Genealogists Magazine:* Indexes
  www.sog.org.uk/genmag/genmag.shtml
  Index to the leading UK genealogical periodical
- *Your Family Tree*
  www.yourfamilytreemag.co.uk
- Index to the *Genealogist,* vols. 1 to 7
  members.pcug.org.au/~bthompso/natlib/geneal.txt
  Index to early issues of an important journal which began
  publication in 1877, available according to the web-page at the
  National Library of Australia - but also in many other large
  reference libraries

- Index to the *Northern Genealogist* Vols. 1 to 6
  members.pcug.org.au/~bthompso/natlib/northgen.txt
  The *Northern genealogist* was published 1895-1903, but has information which may still be useful.
- Archaeologia Cantiana
  www.kentarchaeology.org.uk/Research/Pub/ArchCant/ Intro.htm
  Index to an important county historical journal, which includes some useful articles on family history. Full-text promised.
- *The New England Historical and Genealogical Register*
  www.newenglandancestors.org/research/database/register/ default.asp
  Subscription required. This journal contains numerous articles on English families

Latin
- Latin: in depth guides for learning Latin
  www.nationalarchives.gov.uk/Latin/
- Latin Dictionary and Grammar Aid
  www.nd.edu/~archives/latgramm.htm
- Latin in Parish Records
  www.genuki.org.uk/big/LatinNotes.html

Local History
- How to Research Local History
  www.nationalarchives.gov.uk/localhistory/
- English Local History: a note for beginners
  www.nationalarchives.gov.uk/catalogue/researchguidesindex.asp
  Click title
- British Association for Local History
  www.balh.co.uk
- Sources for British and Irish Local History at Lambeth Palace Library
  www.lambethpalacelibrary.org/holdings/Guides/ loc_history.html
- *Local History Magazine*
  www.local-history.co.uk/
  Includes contents lists, directory of local history societies, and much useful information

Look-ups
- A list of British Isles Genealogy Look-up Sites on the Internet
  freepages.genealogy.rootsweb.com/~goudied/uk_lookups.html
- Books We Own List: a look-up resource for international genealogical research
  www.rootsweb.com/~bwo/
  Lists books which volunteers are willing to search for you.
- UK Genealogy: Lookup Exchanges
  www.ukgenealogy.co.uk/lookup.htm
  Links to pages for most English counties
- UK Look-Up Exchange Index
  aztecrose.tripod.com/LookupExchange.htm
  Lists separate pages for most counties
- Random Acts of Genealogical Kindness
  www.raogk.org
  Lookup site
- Reciprocal Research
  www.allnamesuk.co.uk/recip/recip.htm

Maps
- A directory of UK Map Collections
  www.cartography.org.uk/Pages/Publicat/Ukdir/
- Ordnance Survey
  www.ordnancesurvey.co.uk/oswebsite
  View maps on-line
- Old-Maps.co.uk
  www.old-maps.co.uk
  Historical map archive

Medals *see also* under 'Seamen' *&* 'Soldiers' in Chapter 9
- Civilian Gallantry Medals
  www.nationalarchives.gov.uk/catalogue/researchguidesindex.asp
  Click title
- Britain: Claiming British Medals
  www.geocities.com/dco700/Britain.htm
- UK Medals
  www.stephen-stratford.co.uk/uk_medals.htm
  Summary of medals and awards *etc.*
- George Cross Database
  www.gc-database.co.uk
  Civilian award for bravery since 1940

- Life Saving Awards Research Society
  www.lsars.pwp.blueyonder.co.uk
  Click 'medal rolls and citations' for list of life saving awards by the Royal Humane Society

Missing Persons
- Finding People
  www.ariadne.ac.uk/issue20/search-engines/
  How to use search engines to do it on the internet
- Finding People: phone numbers, e-mail addresses, mailing addresses, places, etc.
  www.cyndislist.com/finding.htm
- Gone Missing UK
  www.gonemissing.co.uk
- Lookup UK.com
  www.lookupuk.com/main.html
  For tracing missing friends and relatives; also includes pages for adoptees
- Lost Cousins: putting relatives in touch
  www.lostcousins.com
- People Trace
  www.peopletrace.com
- The Salvation Army Family Tracing: Looking for Adult Relatives
  www.salvationarmy.org.uk/en/departments/familytracing/Home.htm
- Tracing Living People
  www.bl.uk/collections/social/spis_tlp.html
- Tracing Missing Persons
  www.familyrecords.gov.uk/frc/pdfs/missing_persons.pdf

Orphans
- NCH: Access to records F.A.Q.
  www.nch.org.uk/information/index.php?i=195

Parish, The
- The English Parish
  trushare.com/75AUG01/AU01PAR1.htm
  Continued at **/76SEP01/SE01PARZ.htm**
- The English Civil and Ecclesiastical Parish
  www.metadyne.co.uk/Parish.html
  Detailed explanation of administrative areas in local government

- Genealogy Index: Glossary of Terms
  www.mdlp.co.uk/genweb/glossary.htm
  Definitions of term used in parish history

Peerage, Baronetage & Gentry *see also* Royalty
- Armigerous Ancestors Index
  www.achievements.co.uk/services/arm/index.php
  Index to a collection of 16-17th c. pedigrees. Fee-based.
- A Biographical Peerage of the Empire of Great Britain
  www.bigenealogy.com/peerage/
- Burke's Peerage and Gentry
  www.burkes-peerage.net/
- Burke's Peerage and Baronetage Genealogical and Heraldic Dictionary
  content.ancestry.co.uk/iexec/?htx=BookList&dbid=8487
  Subscription required
- Debrett's Baronetage of England
  www.accessgenealogy.com/baronets
  Originally published 1828.
- The English Peerage (1790)
  www.genuki.org.uk/big/eng/History/Barons/
- The Peerage.com: a Genealogical Survey of the Peerage of Britain as well as the Royal Families of Europe
  www.thepeerage.com
- Peerage of the United Kingdom and Ireland. Volumes I-IV
  content.ancestry.co.uk/iexec/?htx=List&dbid=6717
  Subscription required. From Cokayne's *The Complete peerage*. 1910-16
- Peerages in Order of Precedence
  www3.dcs.hull.ac.uk/genealogy/royal/peerage.html
- Some Corrections and Additions to the *Complete Peerage*
  www.medievalgenealogy.org.uk/cp/index.shtml
- Hereditary Title.com
  www.hereditarytitles.com
- Landed Gentry of Great Britain and Ireland
  content.ancestry.co.uk/iexec/?htx=List&dbid=6625
  Subscription required
- Burke's Commoners of Great Britain and Ireland
  www.ancestry.co.uk/iexec/?htx=List&dbid=6625
  Subscription required

- United Kingdom County Families
  content.ancestry.co.uk/exec/?htx=List&dbid=8628
  Subscription required. Collection of pedigrees published in 1899
- England and Wales Visitations vols. I, III-XIV
  content.ancestry.com/iexec/?htx=List&dbid=6632
  Subscription required. Collection of pedigrees of the Gentry
  (nothing to do with heraldic visitations)
- Obituary Prior to 1800, volume 1
  www.worldvitalrecords.com/
                        indexinfo.aspx?ix=qcd278__volume__1
  Database based on a printed work by Sir William Musgrave. Four
  further volumes

Kent
- County Genealogies: Pedigrees of the Families of the County of
  Kent
  content.ancestry.com/iexec/?htx=BookList&dbid=28684
  Subscription required

Pembrokeshire
- Pembrokeshire Families
  content.ancestry.com/iexec/?htx=List&dbid=8498
  Subscription required

Photographs
- Dating Old Photographs
  genealogy.about.com/cs/photodating
- Photography and Genealogy
  www.ajmorris.com/roots/photo/pg.php
  Study of old photographs
- Researching old photographs
  www.webyfl.com/index.asp?PageAction=Custom&ID=42

Poles
- Tracing Polish Ancestors
  www.staffordshire.gov.uk/leisure/archives/
          familyhistoryresources/TracingPolishAncestors.htm

Quakers
- Early Cumberland and Westmoreland Friends: a series of
  biographical sketches of early members of the Society of Friends
  content.ancestry.com/iexec/?htx=BookList&dbid=29691
  Subscription required

Red Cross
- British Red Cross Museum and Archives
  www.redcross.org.uk/standard.asp?id=2623
  Includes pages on its collections, prisoners of war, personnel
  records, *etc.*

Roman Numerals
- How to Read Roman Numerals
  www.nationalarchives.gov.uk/catalogue/researchguidesindex.asp
  Click title

Royalty
- British Monarchy
  www.royal.gov.uk
  Includes pages on the Royal Archives
- Kings and Queens of England and Scotland (and some of the
  people around them)
  www.genuki.org.uk/big/royalty
- Royal and Noble Genealogical Data on the Web
  www3.dcs.hull.ac.uk/public/genealogy/GEDCOM.html
- RoyaList Online: a royal genealogy database
  www.royalist.info

Strays
- The New National Strays Index
  www.ffhs.org.uk/projects/strays.php
  Description of an index to 'stray' entries in parish registers, census
  returns, monumental inscriptions, etc.
- UK Strays Abroad
  www.familyhistoryonline.net/database/FFHSstrays.shtml
  Found in various records. Pay per view database
- Dorset Strays Index
  www.familyhistoryonline.net/database/DorsetFHSStrays.htm
  Pay per view database

- Herefordshire Strays
  www.familyhistoryonline.net/database/HerefsFHSstrays.shtml
  Pay per view
- Somerset and Dorset Strays Index
  www.familyhistoryonline.net/database/SDFHSstrays.shtml
  Pay per view
- Suffolk Strays
  www.familyhistoryonline.net/database/SFKStrays.shtml
  Pay per view database
- Sussex Strays
  www.familyhistoryonline.net/database/SussexFHGStrays.shtml
  Pay per view
- Wiltshire Strays Index
  www.familyhistoryonline.net/database/WiltsFHSStrays.shtml
  Pay per view
- Yorkshire Strays Index
  www.familyhistoryonline.net/database/YorksGFHSstrays.shtml
  Pay per view
- Yorkshire Strays
  members.lycos.co.uk/Carole__Clyde/
  From the 1851 and 1881 censuses

Surname Origins
- British Family Names: their origin and meaning, with lists of
  Scandinavian, Frisian, Anglo-Saxon and Norman Names
  content.ancestry.co.uk/iexec/?htx=BookList&dbid=28526
  Subscription required
- A Dictionary of English and Welsh Surnames
  content.ancestry.co.uk/iexec/?htx=BookList&dbid=28527
  Subscription required
- English Surnames: their sources and significations
  content.ancestry.co.uk/iexec/?htx=BookList&dbid=28528
  Subscription required. From the book by C.W.E. Beardsley
  published in 1875
- Medieval Names Archive
  www.s-gabriel.org/names/
  www.panix.com/~mittle/names
  Many pages on European names, including one on 'English, Old
  English and Anglo-Norman Names'

- Modern British Surnames: a resource guide to distribution and
  frequency
  homepages.newnet.co.uk/dance/webpjd
- The Relevance of Surnames in Genealogy
  www.sog.org.uk/leaflets/surnames.pdf
- Surname Profiler
  www.spatial-literacy.org/UCLnames
  Surname distribution
- Surname Thesaurus
  www.namethesaurus.com/Thesaurus/Search.aspx
  For checking alternative spellings
- What's in a Name? Your Link to the Past
  www.bbc.co.uk/history/familyhistory/get__started/
  surnames__01.shtml

Cornwall
- Cornish Surnames
  freepages.history.rootsweb.com/~kernow/
  Dictionary

Gloucestershire
- Gloucestershire Names and their Occurrence
  www.grahamthomas.com/glocnames.html

Wales
- Welsh Names and Surnames
  www.users.qwest.net/~butchmatt/WelshNames&Surnames.htm
  General discussion of naming practices

Titanic
- The Titanic
  www.nationalarchives.gov.uk/catalogue/
  researchguidesindex.asp
  Click title

Victoria County Histories
- Victoria County History
  www.victoriacountyhistory.ac.uk

Womens History
- Genesis: developing access to women's history sources in the British Isles
  www.genesis.ac.uk/
  Includes guide to sources on women's history

World War I
- Lost Generation
  www.channel4.com/lostgeneration
- Records of the First World War: Home Front
  www.bedfordshire.gov.uk/CommunityAndLiving/
              ArchivesAndRecordOffice/GuidesToCollections/
              WorldWarOneHomeFrontRecords.aspx
  In Bedfordshire, but indicative of what may be found elsewhere
- Leeds University Library Liddle Collection
  www.leeds.ac.uk/library/spcoll/liddle/
  First World War archive including letters, diaries and other first-hand accounts of the war
- Women's Services, First World War
  www.nationalarchives.gov.uk/catalogue/researchguidesindex.asp
  Click title

World War II
- Home Front: Second World War 1939-1945
  www.nationalarchives.gov.uk/catalogue/researchguidesindex.asp
  Click title
- Women in World War II
  www.familyrecords.gov.uk/focuson/womeninuniform/
              wwii_intro.htm

11. Professional Services, Booksellers, etc.

A. Professional Genealogists
If you want to employ a professional genealogist, you should first read:
- Employing a Professional Researcher: a practical guide
  www.sog.org.uk/leaflets/researcher.pdf

Many professionals have their own web pages. These are not listed here, but many can be found using Cyndis List or Genealogy Pro (see below). The best way to locate a professional is to check the list of members of A.G.R.A., or to ask the relevant record office for a list of researchers who regularly use their resources. Some record offices include lists of professional genealogists on their web pages. A number of national and international web page listings are available:
- A.G.R.A: Association of Genealogists and Researchers in Archives
  www.agra.org.uk
  Includes list of members
- Expert Genealogy Professionals
  www.expertgenealogy.com/
  List of professional genealogists
- Independent Researchers
  www.nationalarchives.gov.uk/irlist
  At The National Archives
- Genealogy Pro
  genealogypro.com/
  List of professionals
- Professional Researchers, Volunteers & other Research Services
  www.Cyndislist.com/profess.htm

B. Booksellers, CD Suppliers, *etc.*
Quite a number of booksellers, publishers, etc. now have a web presence. In addition to the pages listed below, you should also check out the pages of family history societies listed in chapter 4, most of which include an online bookstall. Many of these societies also have stands on Genfair, the major online family history fair. An increasing number of stands are also becoming available at the Parish

Chest, another virtual fair. Other sites with a broad range of books available include the Internet Genealogical Bookshop, which offers the personal assistance of the author of this book, the Family History Partnership, and the Family History Bookshop. Many general booksellers also sell genealogical books, but these are not listed here (except for a number of second-hand sites). Specialist booksellers are best able to offer advice on your genealogical book needs.

- Genealogy Reviews
  www.genealogyreviews.co.uk
  Reviews of books, CDs, software, *etc*
- Abebooks. co.uk
  www.abebooks.co.uk
  Books from second-hand dealers
- Amazon
  www.amazon.com
  Innumerable new and second hand books from many dealers
- Ambra Books
  www.localhistory.co.uk/ambra
  Antiquarian bookseller, specialising in S.W.England
- Ancestor Travel
  www.ancestortravel.com
  Specialist genealogical travel agents
- Ancestral Routes
  www.ancestral-routes.co.uk
  Publishers of basic guides
- Anguline Research Archive
  anguline.co.uk
  CD publishers
- Antiqbook: Book Dealers in Britain and Ireland
  www.antiqbook.co.uk
- Archive Britain: Genealogical Resources
  www.its-your-history.com/Genealogical_Resources.50.0.html
  CD publisher
- Archive CD Books
  www.archivecdbooks.com/
  Innumerable CD's available
- Archived Books
  www.tiO.com/archivedbooks/
  CD publisher

- Back to Roots UK
  www.backtoroots.co.uk
  CD publishers
- Biblioz.Com: the Booksearch Wizard
  www.biblioz.com
  Database of the stock of hundreds of second-hand book dealers
- Bookfinder.com
  www.bookfinder.com
- Brian Jones: family and local history research
  www.brianjoneswry.com
  Publisher of sources for Yorkshire, *etc.*
- British Data Archive
  www.britishdataarchive.com
  CD publishers, especially census data
- C. W. & S. Parkinson Genealogical Storage
  www.cwsparkinson.co.uk
  Stationery suppliers for genealogists
- Chapel Books
  www.chapelbooks.co.uk
  Second-hand bookseller
- Chapel Books Deeds and Documents Index
  www.familyhistoryonline.net/database/ChapelBooksDeeds.shtml
  Index to deeds *etc.,* for sale. Pay per view
- Computer Searchable CDrom Versions of Old and Rare Yorkshire Books
  blunham.com/CDroms/
  cdroms.blunham.com
- Chapman Record Cameos
  www.genuki.org.uk/big/Chapman.html
  List of useful introductory guides by Colin Chapman
- Cornwall Legacy
  www.cornwalllegacy.com
  Details of parish register and other transcripts for sale
- Dartmoor Press
  www.dartmoorpress.clara.net
  Specialist publisher of Devon source material
- David Wright
  www.canterhill.co.uk/davideastkent
  Author/publisher of guides to Kent genealogy

- Digital Archives
  www.digitalarchives.co.uk
  Maps on CD
- Drake Software: specialised programs and data for the discerning genealogist
  www.drake-software.co.uk
- Family History Bookshop
  www.familyhistorybookshop.co.uk
- Family History Fairs
  members.aol.com/aquarterma/familyhistoryfairs.html
- Family History Indexes
  www.fhindexes.co.uk
  Details of the range of indexes compiled by Stuart Tamblin, e.g. militia musters, 1781-2, criminal registers, *etc.*
- The Family History Partnership
  www.familyhistorypartnership.co.uk
  Publishers and booksellers
- The Family History Shop & Library
  www.jenlibrary.u-net.com/
  Specialist in Norfolk and Suffolk genealogical books
- Fetch Book. Info
  www.fetchbook.info
  New and used books from many booksellers
- Francis Boutle Publishers
  www.francisboutle.co.uk
  Publishers of a few genealogical books
- Genealogy Source Catalog
  genealogysourcecatalog.com
  Family history on eBay
- Genfair
  www.genfair.com
  Virtual fair, including stands of numerous family history societies, publishers, and other suppliers. Run by the Federation of Family History Societies
- Genealogy Printers
  www.genealogyprinters.com
  Printers of family trees
- Genealogy Warehouse
  www.genealogical.com/
  Site of the Genealogical Publishing Company; primarily American, but including many titles relevant to English research.
- Gibson Guides: Location Guides for Family and Local Historians, by Jeremy Gibson and others
  www.genuki.org.uk/big/Gibson.html
  Lists an important series of source guides
- Google Book Search
  books.google.com/
  E-books online; includes some of interest to genealogists
- Gould Genealogy
  www.gould.com.au/
  Click 'England/Britain'. The largest genealogical bookshop in Australia
- Heraldic Media
  www.heraldicmedia.com
  Books & Cds
- Hawgood Books
  www.hawgood.co.uk/books.htm
  Author of books on genealogical computing
- Heraldry Today
  www.heraldrytoday.co.uk/
  Bookshop, new and secondhand
- Hudson History of Settle
  www.users.daelnet.co.uk/hudson-history
  Publishers and booksellers of Lancashire and Yorkshire local history
- Independent Booksellers Network
  www.ibooknet.co.uk
- Internet Genealogical Bookshop
  www.stuartraymond.co.uk
- JiGraH Resources
  www.jigrah.co.uk
  Genealogical printers, CD publishers, web page designers, *etc.*
- MM Publications
  www.parishchest.com/en-gb/dept_1205.html
  Publishers of directories and various other sources on microfiche

- The Microfilm Shop
  www.microfilm.com
  Supplies of microfilm, readers, *etc.* Includes useful articles on the advantages and disadvantages of microfilm, digitisation, *etc.*
- Midlands Historical Data
  www.midlandshistoricaldata.org/
  CD publishers covering Shropshire, Staffordshire, Warwickshire and Worcestershire
- Morgan Publications
  homepages.tesco.net/~morganpublications/morganpu.html
  Publishers of Celtic genealogy and heraldry
- My History
  www.my-history.co.uk
  Genealogical booksellers, CD suppliers, *etc.*
- Northamptonshire
  www.northants1841.fsnet.co.uk/
  CD indexes for the county
- Northfiche
  www.jwillans.freeserve.co.uk/
  Publishers of orginal sources for Co.Durham and Northumberland
- OnegeneUk
  www.onegene.co.uk
  Software & data CDs
- The Parish Chest
  www.parishchest.com
  On line fair; stands from a variety of suppliers
- PBN Publications
  www.pbnpublications.com
  Publishers of original sources for Sussex
- Phillimore
  www.phillimore.co.uk
  Major local history and genealogy publisher
- Regional Books
  cnb-host3.clickandbuild.com/cnb/shop/regionalbooks/
  Second-hand books on the history of Northern England
- Robert Blatchford Publishing
  www.genealogical.co.uk
  Publishers of the *Family and local history handbook*
- S & N Genealogy Supplies
  www.genealogysupplies.com
  CDs & software supplies

- Salopian Family History Company
  www.genfind.co.uk
  www.salopian.info
  Publishers of CD's and downloadable census transcripts for Shropshire
- Shire Publications
  www.shirebooks.co.uk
  Publishers of genealogy, local history and folklore
- Sigma Books
  www.sigmabooks.fsnet.co.uk
  Publications on Suffolk & Berkshire for the genealogist and local historian
- Staunton Park Genealogy Centre
  www.stauntoninfo.co.uk/index2.htm
  Hampshire publishers
- Steve Garton Genealogy
  www.stevejgarton.co.uk
  CD publishers and map sellers
- Stepping Stones
  www.stepping-stones.co.uk
  Directories and the census on CD; also has some censuses online
- John Townsend Genealogy Books
  www.johntownsend.demon.co.uk
  Specialist second-hand bookseller in genealogy and local history
- Trueflare Ltd
  hometown.aol.com/rjcindex/
  Details of R.J.Cottrell's *Apprenticeship (binding) indexes for the Company of Watermen and Lightermen of the River Thames 1691-1949;* also of his *Thames & Medway riverside parish series* of parish register transcriptions
- TWR Computing
  www.twrcomputing.co.uk/
  Publishers of CD's; stockists of computer programs for family history
- UK Book World
  ukbookworld.com
  Second-hand books from many dealers
- Used Books Search
  www.usedbooksearch.co.uk
  Linked to thousands of booksellers

- Yesteryears Genealogy Supplies
  www.yesteryearsgen.com
  CD publishers
- Yorkshire Ancestors.com
  www.yorkshireancestors.com
  Residential library and CD publishers
- Yorkshire Indexers
  www.yorkshireindexers.co.uk/
  Publishers of various Yorkshire indexes and transcripts on CD
- Your Old Books & Maps
  www.youroldbooksandmaps.co.uk
  CD publishers.

C. Software Suppliers
- Which Genealogy Software Program is Best?
  genealogy.about.com/cs/genealogysoftware/a/software.htm
- Graham's Genealogy Links: shareware and free software to download
  www.genealogy.hampshire.org.uk/software.html
- Ancestral Author
  www.ancestralauthor.com
  Programme for creating PDF files from Gedcom files
- Brothers Keeper
  www.bkwin.com
- The Church of Jesus Christ of Latter Day Saints: Family History: Software & Databases
  www.ldscatalog.com/
  Scroll down to 'Family History' and click 'software & Databases'. Includes details of Personal Ancestral File software. Also click 'software downloads'.
- Clooz: the electronic filing cabinet for genealogical records
  www.clooz.com
- Cumberland Family Software
  www.cf-software.com/
- Custodian
  www.custodian3.co.uk
  Family tree software publisher
- Dr. Alex Software
  www.dralex.com/builder/home/

- Family Historian
  www.family-historian.co.uk
- Family Tree Legends
  www.familytreelegends.com
- Family Tree Maker
  www.familytreemaker.com
- Geditcom: Genealogy Software for the Macintosh
  www.geditcom.com
- GenboxTM Family History
  www.genbox.com
- Genopro
  www.genopro.com
- Html Pedigree
  www.htmlpedigree.com
  Software for creating web pages from GEDCOM data
- Legacy Family Tree
  www.legacyfamilytree.com/
- Northern Hills Software LLC
  www.northernhillssoftware.com
- Passage Express
  www.familyhistorycd.com
- Pedigree Soft.com
  www.pedigresoft.com
- Relatively Yours 3: the complete genealogy system
  www.relativelyyours.com
- Rootsmagic
  www.rootsmagic.com
- SpanSoft
  www.spansoft.org
- Tapperware
  www.tapperware.com
  Details of My Roots software
- Wholly Genes Software
  www.whollygenes.com

Subject Index

Abbreviations 101
Absent Voters Lists 47, 48
Accountants 80
Actors 100
Administrative Areas 101, 110
Adoption 101
Agricultural Labourers 104
Airmen 80
Alien Registration Cards 48
Ancestral File 43
Ancient Petitions 48
Anglo-Indian Ancestors 102
Apothecaries 81, 89
Apprentices 81, 82, 89, 94, 116
Archbishops 83
Archer, Isaac 55
Architects 81
Archives 10-16, 18-21
Army 12, 90, 97-99, 101
Army Lists, Indian 86
Artists 68, 81
Assize Records 53
Assizes 85
Asylums 89
Attorneys 81, 88

Bankers 81
Bankrupts 81
Baptists 90
Baronetage 110
Bastardy 68, 73, 74
Battle of Trafalgar 96
Bibliography 8, 9, 39, 60, 69
Biographical Dictionaries 102
Biography 20
Births, Marriages and Deaths 11, 43, 48, 52, 75, 97, 104
Bishops Registers 52
Blacksmiths 81
Boatmen 81

Boer War 16, 30
Book Trades 82
Bookbinders 80
Bookplates 48
Books 8, 9, 27, 28, 31, 113-116
Books, Second-Hand 114-116
Booksellers 113-115
Booth's Survey 48
Boxers 82
Boyds Marriage Index 61
Brass Rubbings 48
Brewers 82
Bricklayers 80
Brickmakers 80
Bridgemasters Accounts 63
Broadcasters 86
Brushmakers 80, 82
Burnt Documents 98
Bus & Cab Workers 80
Business Records 12, 48
Butchers 82

Canal Boatmen 29, 81
Capital Punishment 84, 87
Carpenters 80, 82
Carriers 82
Cartularies 47-49
Carvers 80
CDs 114-117
Cemeteries 30
Census 11, 22, 30, 34, 36-38, 43, 47, 50-52, 96, 112, 114, 116
Census, Pre-1841 51
Chancery 53, 54
Change of Name 102
Chantry Certificates 49
Chapman Codes 101
Chapman Record Cameos 114
Chartists 82, 102
Chemists 82
Child Migrants 102
Christian Names 102
Church Archives 12
Church Records 12, 51, 52, 55

Churches 105
Churchwardens Accounts 34, 52
Circus Performers 82
Civil Engineers 82
Civil Registration 30, 47, 48, 52, 53
Civil Servants 83
Civil Servants, Indian 86
Civil War 98
Clandestine Marriages 65
Clergy 29, 51, 80, 83
Clock & Watchmakers 83
Coal Miners 13, 29, 83
Coastguards 29, 83, 84
Coe, William 55
Compositors 80
Computer Books 115
Computers in genealogy 27, 31, 102
Conscientious Objectors 84
Contiguous Parishes 103
Convicts, Criminals, Prisoners, *etc* 29, 53, 84, 85, 115
Copyright 30
Coroners Records 53
County Maps 101
Courses 103
Court Records 47, 53, 54
Courtiers 93
Courts Martial 98, 99
Crests 107
Crew Lists 18, 94, 95
Cricketers 85
Crimean War 30, 90
Customs & Excise Officers 85, 86
Cyclists 86

D.N.A. 103
Dade Registers 65
Dates & Chronology 103
Datestones 54
Death Duties 54, 72
Debtors 81
Deeds & Charters 48, 49, 56, 57, 76, 77
Deeds Registries 19, 55

Dentists 80, 86
Deserted Villages 30
Deserters 98
Diaries 55, 113
Dictionary of National Biography 102
District Registrars 52
Divers 86
Divorce Records 55
Dockyard Workers 86
Doctors 80, 89
Domesday Book 55
Dormant Funds 103
Drovers 86

East Indiamen 86
Ecclesiastical Visitations 55
Educational Records 55
Electoral registers 36, 47, 56
Electrical Engineers 86
Emigrants & Emigration 14, 29, 83, 85, 95, 102-105
Enclosure Records 56, 76
Entertainers 86
Equity 54
Era, The 100
Estate Agents Records 56
Estate Records 12, 13, 51, 56, 57, 60
Evacuees 105
Events 31, 105, 115
Exchequer 54
Executions 84, 87
Eyres 54

Faculty Office 61
Fairs 115
Fake Titles 105
Family Bibles 57
Family Histories 9
Family History Centers 8
Family History Societies 21, 23-26, 115
Feet of Fines 57
Field Books 57

Fire Insurance Records 57
First Fleet 85
Fishermen 86
Flood Claims 57
Footballers 86
Foundlings 86
Freedmen 29
Freeholders 57
Freemasons 12, 86
Freemen 57
Funeral 105

Gaol Registers 18
Gardeners & Horticulturalists 86, 87
Gas Men 87
Gateways 5
Gazetteers 105, 106
Gedcom 106, 117
Genealogical Research Directory 43
Genealogists, Professional 113
Gentleman's Magazine 63
Gentry 80, 110, 111
Germans 106
Gibson Guides 115
Gilders 80
Glebe Terriers 58
Good Practice 106
Great Sessions 54
Greffe Records 20
Gun Makers 87
Gypsies 31, 87

Hackney Coachmen 87
Handwriting 31, 106
Hangmen 87
Hardwicke's Marriage Act 1753 65
Hatters 29
Hearth Tax 58, 75
Hemp & Flax Growers 87
Heraldic Visitations 58, 59, 107
Heraldry 31, 105-107
Heralds 87

Higglers Licences 73
Highwaymen 91
History 13, 29
Home Children 29, 30, 104, 107
Home Guard 98
Hood, H.M.S. 97
Horse Racing Fraternity 87
Hospital Records 11, 59, 91
House Decorators 80
House History 107, 108
Huguenots 12, 43, 108

I.G.I. (International Genealogical Index) 11, 43, 59, 60
Immigrants 108
Indexing 22
Inheritance Dispute 53
Innkeepers 29, 87, 88
Inquisitions Post Mortem 59
Institutions 31, 108
Insurance Records 59
Internees 88
Internet 7
Interregnum 60
Irish 23, 108
Ironfounders 80

Jacobite Records 60
Jews 30, 31, 108
Jockeys 87
Joiners 80
Journalists 88
Journals 22, 63, 106, 108
Justices of the Peace 60

King's Bench 54

Land Tax 60
Land Tax Commissioners 88
Latin 109
Law for Genealogists 31
Law List 88
Lawyers 88, 89
Leather Workers 89

Libraries 10-20, 117
Lighthouse Keepers 89, 94
Liverymen 89
Lloyds Captains Register 94
Local History 12, 109
Local History Magazine 109
London Gazette 58
Look-ups 109
Lunatics 89

Maggs, James 55
Mailing Lists 27, 43
Manorial Documents Register 60
Manorial Records 60, 61
Maps 76, 101, 109, 115, 116
Marine Insurance Record 61
Marriage Licences 61
Marriages 61
Mathematicians 89
Medals 63, 95, 99, 109
Medical Licences 89
Medical Men 89
Medical Register 89
Medieval genealogy 8, 27, 29, 31, 49, 98
Members of Parliament 89
Merchant Navy 29, 94, 95
Merchant Taylors 89
Merchants 89
Message Boards 27
Methodist Records 12
Microfiche 115
Microfilm 115, 116
Midwives Registers 61
Militia Attestations 98
Militia Rolls 62, 98, 115
Miners 80, 90
Missing Persons 110
Monumental Inscriptions 16, 30, 34, 37, 47, 49, 62
Mormons 105
Motor Vehicle Registration 62
Municipal Officers 90
Municipal Records 62, 63

Music Hall 100
Muster Rolls 37, 98

Napoleonic Wars 96, 98
National Burials Index 47
National Farm Survey 63
National Strays Index 111
Naturalization Records 63
New England Historical & Genealogical Register 109
Newsgroups 27
Newspapers 11, 16, 18, 30, 63, 64
Nobility 30
Nonconformist Registers 14, 64
Nonconformists 12
Norris, Henry 60
Notes & Queries 63
Nurses 90, 91

Oakes, James 55
Oath Rolls 64, 65
Obituaries 30
Occupations 29, 30, 80
Old Bailey 54
One Name Studies 21, 43
One Place Studies 31
Orphans 110
Ostle, John 55
Outlaws 91
Overseas Research 8, 48

Painters 80
Papermakers 29, 91
Parish Clerks 91
Parish Law 31
Parish Magazines 65
Parish Records 35, 65
Parish Registers 14, 16, 18, 22, 23, 30, 34, 36, 37, 41, 47, 48, 58, 61, 65, 114, 116
Parish, The 110
Passenger Lists 65, 66, 104, 107
Passport Records 66
Patients 91

Peculiars 72
Pedigrees 42, 43, 111
Peerage 110
Pensions 98
Performing Arts 100
Persi 108
Phillimore 65
Phone Books 66
Phone Directories 12
Photographers 29, 30, 91
Photographs 29, 30, 62, 66, 111
Physicians 89
Picture-frame Makers 80
Pilots 92
Pipemakers 29
Place Names 105
Plasterers 80
Poles 111
Police 92
Pollbooks 66, 67
Poor Law 14, 31, 67, 68, 74, 75, 108
Portraits 66, 68
Postcards 69
Postmen 12, 29, 92
Potters 92
Printing Workers 80
Prison Officers 92
Prisoners of War 81, 92
Prisons 108
Probate Inventories 72
Probate Records 69-72
Psychiatrists & Psychologists 93
Public Libraries 10

Quaker Records 12, 73
Quakers 111
Quarrymen 80, 93
Quarter Sessions 21, 73, 84
Query Boards 27

Railwaymen 29, 30, 80, 93
Rate Books 73
Recognizances 73, 88
Record Offices 10-21, 106

Record Societies 9
Refugees 93
Regimental Histories 99
Regiments 30
Register Offices 52
Regnal Years 103
Removal Orders 73-75
Requests, Court of 54
Return of Owners of Land 73, 74
Roman Catholic registers 49
Roman Catholics 15, 49, 74
Roman Numerals 111
Royal Household Servants 93
Royal Marines 93
Royal Naval Volunteer Reserve 97
Royal Navy 94-96
Royal Warrant Holders 93
Royalist Composition Papers 74
Royalists 60
Royalty 111

Sacrament Certificates 64
School Records 74
Schools 31
Scriveners 93
Seamen (Merchant & Royal Navy)
    12, 30, 80, 94-96
Search Engines 7, 110
Search Techniques 7
Servants 97, 103
Service Records 96, 98, 99
Settlement Examinations 74
Shareholders 97
Shareware 117
Ship Owners 97
Singers 100
Sneyd Papers 13
Software 102, 114, 117
Soldiers, Militiamen, etc. 12, 30, 63,
    97-99
Solicitors 81, 88
Star Chamber 54
State Papers 75
Stationery 114

Steam Engine Makers 80, 99
Stockbrokers 100
Stonemasons 80
Strays 111, 112
Street Indexes 106
Students 100
Subsidies 37, 75
Sugar Bakers & Refiners 100
Supreme Court 54
Surgeons 89
Surname Lists 37, 43, 45
Surname Origins 112
Surnames 27, 28, 31
Surrey Advertiser 64
Surveys 60, 76
Swedenborgians 31

Tax Records 47, 51, 60, 75, 76
Teachers 100
Telephone Directories 77
Temperance Records 76
Terriers 76
Territorials 98
Texts and Calendars 9
Theatre Workers 30, 100
Times, The 63
Titanic 112
Tithe Records 19, 76
Title Deeds 114
Toll Books 77
Tontine Records 77
Trade Directories 9, 34, 36, 37, 43,
    47, 77, 78, 88, 115, 116
Traders 100
Trafalgar Roll 96
Tramway Workers 80
Transcripts 31
Transport Workers 100
Transportees 29, 84, 85
Travel Agents 114
Trivia 28

Union Catalogue (Copac) 10

Valuation Office Records 78, 79
Vehicle Licensing Records 79
Vets 101
Vicar General 61
Victoria County Histories 112
Victoria Cross 99
Victuallers Licences 87, 88
Villages 31
Volunteers 98

War Memorials 12, 79
Wards & Liveries 54
Watchmakers 30
Watermen & Lightermen 29, 30, 81,
    101, 116
Webrings 7
Wedgwood Archives 13
West Briton 64
Whalers 101
Whitley, Roger 55
Wills 11, 14, 18, 34, 69-72
Window Tax 79
Witches 101
Women 90, 113
Woodworkers 80
Workhouses 31, 67, 68, 108
World War I 79, 91, 92, 95, 98, 99,
    113
World War II 79, 90, 91, 95, 99,
    105, 113
Writing Up 31

Yeomanry 98

Institution Index

79th Regiment 30

Abebooks 114
Alex Software, Dr. 117
Ambra Books 114
Ancestors Magazine 108
Ancestors on Board 65
Ancestral Author 117
Ancestral Routes 114
Ancestry.com 42, 47
Anglesey Archives Service 20
Anglesey Library Services 20
Anglo-Austrian Family History Group 21
Anglo-French Family History Society 22
Anglo-German Family History Society 22
Anglo-Italian Family History Society 22
Anguline 114
Archdeaconry Court of Canterbury 70
Archdeaconry Court of London 71
Archdeaconry Court of Nottingham 13
Archdeaconry Court of Surrey 71
Archive Britain 114
Archive CD Books Project 114
Archived Books 114
Archives Council Wales 20
Archives Hub 10
Archives Network Wales 20
Association of Cricket Statisticians & Historians 85
Association of Family History Societies of Wales 26
Association of Football Statisticians 86
Association of Genealogists and Record Agents 113
Audley & District Family History Society 24

B.B.C. 8, 39
Back to Roots 114
Bank of England 69
Baptist Missionary Society 90
Barnsley Archives & Local Studies Dept. 19

Barnsley Family History Society 25
Baronage Press 106
Bath Record Office 18
Bedfordshire & Luton Archives 13
Bedfordshire Family History Society 22
Berkshire Family History Society 22
Berkshire Record Office 13
Berwick upon Tweed Record Office 17
Bethlem Royal Hospital 11
Bexley Local Studies & Archive Centre 15
Biblioz 114
Birmingham & Midland Society for Genealogy & Heraldry 25, 53
Birmingham City Archives 19
Blatchford Publishing 116
Board of Inland Revenue 79
Bodleian Library 13
Bolton Archives 15
Bookplate Society 48
Borthwick Institute of Historical Research 19, 72
Boutle, Francis 115
Bradford Family History Society 25
Bradford Libraries Archives & Information Service 19
Brent Local History & Heritage 16
Brewery History Society 82
Bristol & Avon Family History Society 23
Bristol Record Office 15
Bristol Reference Library 15
British & Foreign School Society 100
British Academy 58
British Association for Local History 109
British Association of Paper Historians 91
British Data Archive 114
British History Online 47
British Home Children Society 107
British Isles Family History Society - U.S.A. 22
British Isles Family History Society of Greater Ottowa 22
British Library 11
British Library Newspaper Library 11
British Postal Museum 92
British Record Society 58, 69

British Records Association 22
British Transport Police 92
Bromley Archives 15
Brothers Keeper 117
BT Archives 12
Buckinghamshire Family History Society 22
Buckinghamshire Genealogical Society 22
Burkes 110
Burntwood Family History Group 24
Burton & Local History Centre 18
Burton on Trent Archives 18
Bury Archive Service 16

Cable & Wireless 82
Calderdale Family History Society 25
Cambridge University 100
Cambridge University Heraldic & Genealogical Society 22
Cambridge University Library 12
Cambridgeshire Archives Service 13
Cambridgeshire Family History Society 22
Cambridgeshire Record Office 15
Camden Local Studies & Archive Centre 16
Canterbury Cathedral Archives 15
Cardiganshire Family History Society 26
Carmarthenshire Archives Service 20
Carmarthenshire Family History Society 26
Catholic Central Library 49
Catholic Family History Society 22, 49
Catholic Record Society 49
Centre for Buckinghamshire Studies 13
Centre for Kentish Studies 15
Centre for Oxfordshire Studies 17
Centre for Research into Freemasonry 86
Ceredigion Archives 20
Channel Islands Family History Society 26
Chapel Books 114
Charterhouse School 74
Cheshire and Chester Archives and Local Studies 13
Chesterfield & Dist. Family History Society 23
Child Migrants Trust 102
Childrens Society 107
Christian Brothers 102

Christs Hospital 104
Church Mission Society 12, 90
Church of England 83
Circus Historical Society 82
City of London Record Office 53
City of Westminster Archives Centre 17
City of York & District Family History Society 26
Cleveland Family History Society 23
Clooz 117
Clwyd Family History Society 26
Coal Mining History Resource Centre 83
College of Arms 12
Commonwealth War Graves Commission 79
Complete Peerage 110
Consignia 12
Consistory Court of London 71
Conwy Archives 20
Copac 10
Cornwall Centre 13
Cornwall Family History Society 22
Cornwall Legacy 114
Cornwall Record Office 13
Corporation of London Libraries 16
Corporation of London Record Office 16
Cotton College 74
Cottrell, R.J. 116
County Archives Research Network 11
Coventry Archives 19
Coventry Family History Society 25
Coventry Local Studies Library 19
Croydon Local Studies & Archives Service 18
Cumberland Family Software 117
Cumbria Archive Service 14
Cumbria Family History Society 22
Curious Fox 28
Custodian 117
Cyndis List 5, 7, 10, 11, 27, 39, 42, 102, 110, 113
Cyngor Gwynedd Council Archives 20

Dartmoor Press 114
Debretts 110
Debt of Honour Register 43
Denbighshire Record Office 20

Derbyshire Family History Society 23
Derbyshire Record Office 14
Devon & Cornwall Record Society 14
Devon Family History Society 23
Devon Library & Information Services 14
Devon Record Office 14
Digital Archives 115
Digital Library of Historical Directories 77
Documents Online 47
Doncaster & District Family History Society 25
Doncaster Archives 19
Dorset Archives Service 14
Dorset Family History Society 23
Dorset History Centre 14
Dr. Williams Library 12
Dudley Archives & Local History 19
Durham Cathedral 106
Durham Record Office 14
Durham University Library 12
Dyfed Family History Society 26

Ealing Local History Centre 16
East Kent Archives Centre 15
East of London Family History Society 24
East Riding of Yorkshire Archives Service 19
East Surrey Family History Society 25
East Sussex Record Office 18
East Yorkshire Family History Society 25
eBay 115
Ely Diocese 12
Enfield Libraries Local History Unite 16
Epsom Family History Group 25
Essex Record Office 14
Essex Society for Family History 23

Fairground Heritage Trust 82
Fal Worldwide Family History 22
Family & Community Historical Research Society 22
Family & Local History Handbook 116
Family & Local History Indexing Group 22
Family Historian 117
Family History Books 115
Family History Indexes 115

Family History Monthly 108
Family History Online 47
Family History Partnership 115
Family History Shop 115
Family History Society of Cheshire 22
Family Records Centre 11
Family Relatives 42
Family Roots 25
Family Search 11
Family Tree Legends 117
Family Tree Magazine 108
Family Tree Maker 117
Federation of Family History Societies 8, 21, 115
Felixstowe Family History Society 25
Fenland Family History Society 22
Fetch Book 115
Find My Past 47
Fleet Air Arm 81
Flintshire Archives 21
Folkestone & District Family History Society 23
Friends House 12
Friends of the Public Record Office 22
Furness Family History Society 23

Garton, Steve 116
Gateshead Libraries 14
Geditcom 117
Gen Circles 42
Genbox 117
Genealogical Publishing Co. 115
Genealogists Magazine 108
Genealogy Links 6
General Register Office 53, 101
Genfair 115
GENi 42
Genopro 117
Genuki 5, 8, 27, 32-41, 43, 47, 50, 105
Genweb 6, 28, 30, 32-41
Glamorgan Record Office 21, 92
Glamorganshire Family History Society 26
Gloucestershire Family History Society 23
Gloucestershire Record Office 14

Google 7, 8, 115
Google Book Search 8
Gould Genealogy 115
Greater Manchester County Record Office 16
Greenwich Heritage Centre 15
Guild of One-Name Studies 42
Guildhall Library 16, 51, 57, 59, 74, 77, 94
Gwent Family History Society 26
Gwent Record Office 21
Gwynedd Family History Society 26

Hackney Archives Department 17
Hammersmith & Fulham Libraries - Archives & Local History 17
Hampshire Genealogical Society 23
Hampshire Record Office 15
Harrow Local History Collection 17
Hartland Archives Project 34
Hastings & Rother Family History Society 25
Haverhill Family History Group 25
Heraldry Society 22
Heraldry Today 115
Herefordshire Archive Service 15
Herefordshire Family History Society 23
Hertfordshire Archives and Local Studies 15
Hertfordshire Family & Population History Society 23
Hillingdon Family History Society 24
Hillingdon Local Studies Archives & Museums Service 17
Historical Manuscripts Commission 84, 94
Hounslow Local Studies and Archives 17
House of Lords Record Office 12
Huddersfield & District Family History Society 25
Huguenot Society 108
Hull City Archives 19
Hull Local Studies Library 19
Huntingdon County Record Office 15
Huntingdonshire Family History Society 23
Hyde Park Family History Centre 11

Imperial War Museum 12
India Office 11

Indian Army 86
Inner Temple 89
Institute of Heraldic and Genealogical Studies 21
Institute of Historical Research 13
Institution of Electrical Engineers 86
Interment.net 62
Internet Genealogical Bookshop 115
Isle of Axholme Family History Society 24
Isle of Man Family History Society 26
Isle of Wight Family History Society 23
Isle of Wight Record Office 15
Islington Local History Centre 17

Jersey Heritage Trust 20
Jewish Genealogical Society of Great Britain 22
Jigrah 115
John Rylands University Library of Manchester 13
Jones, Brian 114

Keele University Library 13
Keighley & Dist. Family History Society 25
Kent Family History Society 23
Kings College London 97

Lambeth Archives Department 18
Lambeth Palace Library 12, 109
Lancashire Family History & Heraldry Society 23
Lancashire Parish Register Society 23
Lancashire Record Office 15
Lancaster Family History Group 23
Latter Day Saints 8, 117
Latter Day Saints. Family History Centres 11
Leeds Local Studies Library 19, 20
Leeds University 13
Legacy 117
Leicester & Rutland Family History Society 24
Lewisham Local Studies & Archives 15
Lichfield Record Office 18
Liddell Hart Centre for Military Archives 97
Liddle Collection 113

Lincoln Consistory Court 71
Lincolnshire Archives 16
Lincolnshire Family History Society 24
Lincolnshire Libraries 16
List & Index Society 11
Liverpool & S.W. Lancashire Family History Society 23
London Borough of Merton Local Studies Centre 18
London Borough of Richmond upon Thames Loc.History & Spec.Col 18
London Borough of Sutton 18
London Consistory Court 71
London Cornish Association 22
London Metropolitan Archives 16, 55, 56, 59, 71, 87, 88, 91, 100, 108
London Westminster & Middlesex Family History Society 24
Lost Cousins 110

Malvern Family History Group 25
Manchester & Lancashire Family History Society 23
Manchester Archives & Local Studies 16
Manchester Regiment 16, 97
Manchester Ship Canal 97
Manx National Library 20
Medway City Ark 15
Memorial University of Newfoundland 95
Merseyside Maritime Museum 95
Methodist Archives and Research Centre 12
Metropolitan Police Service 92
Mid-Norfolk Family History Society 24
Ministry of Defence 96
MM Publications 115
Modern Records Centre 12
Montgomeryshire Genealogical Society 26
Morgan Publications 116
Morley Family History Group 25
MSN Groups 28
My Family 42
My Heritage 42
My History 116
My Roots 117

National Archives 8, 11, 47, 55, 60, 113
National Archives of Australia 102, 104
National Army Museum 12
National Fairground Archives 82
National Inventory of War Memorials 12
National Library of Wales 20
National Maritime Museum 12, 95
National Portrait Gallery 68
National Railway Museum 93
National Register of Archives 11, 48, 55, 81, 84, 86, 88, 94, 97
National Society 100
Naval & Military Press 99
Neath Antiquarian Society 21
New Zealand Society of Genealogists: Welsh Interest Group 26
Newcastle Local Studies Library 17
Newham Archives and Local History 14
Norfolk Family History Society 24
Norfolk Record Office 17
North Cheshire Family History Society 22
North Devon Record Office 14
North Lincolnshire Libraries & Information Services 16
North Meols Family History Society 23
North Tyneside Local Studies 17
North West Kent Family History Society 23
North Yorkshire Archives 19
Northamptonshire Family History Society 24
Northamptonshire Record Office 17
Northern Genealogist 109
Northern Hills 117
Northfiche 116
Northumberland & Durham Family History Society 24
Northumberland Collections Service 17
Nottingham University 13
Nottinghamshire Archives 17
Nottinghamshire Family History Society 24
Nottinghamshire Libraries 17
Nuneaton & North Warwickshire Family History Society 25

Oldham Local Studies and Archives 16

Onegene 116
Original Record 47
Ormskirk & District Family History Society 23
Oxfordshire Family History Society 24
Oxfordshire Record Office 17

Pacific Northwest Cornish Society 22
Palmer Centre for Local Studies & Archives 21
Parish Chest 116
Parish Register Transcription Society 65
Parkinson, C. W. & S. 114
Parliamentary Archives 12
Passage Express 117
PBN Publications 116
Pedigree Soft.com 117
Pembrokeshire Record Office 21
Peterborough & District Family History Society 24
Phillimore 55, 116
Plymouth & West Devon Record Office 14
Plymouth Local & Naval Studies Library 14
Police History Society 92
Pontefract & District Family History Society 25
Portsmouth Records Office 15
Post Office 12
Powys County Archives Office 21
Powys Digital History Project 40
Powys Family History Society 26, 40
Practical Family History 108
Prerogative Court of Canterbury 69, 70
Priaulx Library 20
Pub History Society 87

Quaker Family History Society 22

Railway Ancestors Family History Society 22
Record Office for Leicestershire, Leicester and Rutland 16
Red Cross 111
Redbridge Local Studies and Libraries 14
Regional Books 116
Reigate & District Family History Group 25
Relatively Yours 117

Ripon Historical Society 25
Ripon, Harrogate & District Family History Group 25
Rochdale Local Studies & Archives 16
Romany & Traveller Family History Society 22
Roots UK 47
Roots-L 28
Rootsmagic 117
Rootsweb 5, 7, 8, 27, 42, 43
Rotherham Family History Society 25
Rotherham Metropolitan Borough Archives and Local Studies 20
Royal Air Force 80, 81
Royal Air Force Museum 80
Royal Borough of Kensington & Chelsea Local Studies 17
Royal College of Nursing 90
Royal College of Physicians 89
Royal Flying Corps 80
Royal Historical Society 9
Royal Humane Society 110
Royal Institution of Cornwall 14
Royal Institution of South Wales 21
Royal Marines 93
Royal Naval Air Service 80
Royal Naval Division 96
Royal Navy 96
Royal Photographic Society 91
Rugby Family History Group 25
Rural History Centre 12

S & N 116
Saint Helen Townships Family History Society 23
Saint Pauls Cathedral 51
Salford Diocese 15
Salopian Family History Co. 116
Salvation Army 110
Shakespeare Birthplace Trust 19
Sheffield & District Family History Society 26
Sheffield Archives 20
Sheffield Local Studies Library 20
Shropshire Archives 18
Shropshire Family History Society 24

Sigma Books 116
Société Guernesiaise. Family History Section 26
Société Jersiaise 20
Society of Antiquaries of London 12
Society of Genealogists 8, 21, 105
Somerset & Dorset Family History Society 24
Somerset Archive and Record Service 18
Southampton City Archives 15
Southwark Local History Library 18
SpanSoft 117
Staffordshire and Stoke on Trent Archive Services 18
Staffordshire Historical Collections 47
Staffordshire Record Office 18
State Records Authority of New South Wales 104
Stationers Company 82
Stationers Hall 82
Staunton Park Genealogy Centre 116
Steam Engine Makers Society 99
Stepping Stones 116
Stock Exchange 100
Stoke on Trent City Archives 18
Suffolk Family History Society 25
Suffolk Record Office 18
Sun Fire Office 57
Surrey History Service 18
Sussex Family History Group 25
Sutton Archives and Local Studies 18
Swansea Coalfield Collection 13

Tameside Local Studies & Archives Centre 16
Tameside Local Studies Library 13
Tapperware 117
Thameside Family History Group 23
Torbay Local Studies 14
Tower Hamlets Local story & Archives 17
Townsend, John 116
Trafford Local Studies Centre 16
Trinity House 94
Trueflare 116
Tunbridge Wells Family History Society 23
Turnpike Trustees 82

TWR Computing 116
Tyne & Wear Archives Service 14, 17, 83

UK Book World 116
UKGenealogy 7, 32-39, 41
University College London 12
University of Bristol 100
University of Central Lancashire 103
University of Hull Archives 12
University of Leeds. Brotherton Library 13
University of Leicester. Dept. of English Local History 12
University of Oxford 100
   Balliol College 13
   Bodleian Library 13
University of Southampton. The Hartley Library 13
University of Swansea Library 13
University of Toronto 76

Vestry House Museum Local Studies Library 14
Veterans Agency 99
Voluntary Aid Detachments 91

Wakefield Family History Society 26
Walsall Family History Group 24
Walsall Local History Centre 18
Wandsworth Local History Service 18
Warwickshire County Record Office 19
Warwickshire Family History Society 25
Wayback Machine 8
We Relate 43
West Country Studies Library 14, 48
West Dorset Research Centre 14
West Glamorgan Archive Service 21, 95
West Middlesex Family History Society 24
West Riding Registry of Deeds 19
West Surrey Family History Society 25
West Sussex Local Studies 18
West Sussex Record Office 18
West Yorkshire Archives Service 19
Western Front Association 99
Weston Super Mare Family History Society 24
Wharfedale Family History Group 26

Wholly Genes 117
Wigan Archive Service 16
William Salt Library 18
Wiltshire & Swindon Record Office 19
Wiltshire Family History Society 25
Wolverhampton Archives and Local Studies 18
Women's Army Auxiliary Corps 98
Womens Royal Naval Service 90
Worcestershire Record Office 19
World Connect Project 43
World Family Tree 43
Wrexham Archives Service 21
Wright, David 114

Yahoo 7
Yahoo Groups 28
Yesteryears 117
York City Archives 20
York Minster Library 20
York Reference Library 85
Yorkshire Ancestors 117
Yorkshire Archaeological Society 19
   Family History Section 26
Yorkshire Indexers 117
Your Family Tree 108
Ystradgynlais Family History Society 26

Place Index

Alderney 39

Anglesey 20, 26, 40

Bedfordshire 13, 22, 32, 43, 51, 56, 58, 59, 61, 67, 68, 76, 80, 87, 91, 92, 105, 113
   Bedford 62, 84
   Dunstable 62
   Luton 62

Berkshire 13, 22, 32, 43, 49, 56, 58, 68, 70, 91, 116
   Cumnor 33
   Hungerford 70
   Wantage 70
   Windsor 63

Breconshire 26, 40
   Ystradgynlais 26

Buckinghamshire 13, 22, 33, 43, 48, 57, 67, 73, 77, 87
   Aylesbury 84
   Broughton 33
   Eton 63
   Milton Keynes 33
   Missenden Abbey 48
   Newport Pagnell 92

Caernarvonshire 20, 26, 40, 73, 88
   Bangor Diocese 52
   Carnarvon 100
   Conway 20

Cambridgeshire 12, 13, 22, 33, 43, 66, 70, 87, 88, 103
   Ely Diocese 12
   Isle of Ely 22
   Wisbech 13

Cardiganshire 9, 20, 26, 40

Carmarthenshire 20, 26, 40

Channel Islands 26, 39, 46, 95

Cheshire 13, 22, 33, 44, 55, 70, 76, 93, 107
   Chester 13, 57, 90
   Tameside 13

Cheshire, North 22

Cornwall 13, 22, 33, 44, 49, 58, 63, 70, 90, 93, 104, 112
   Bodmin Moor 33
   Fal 22
   Porthcurno 82
   West Penwith 33, 88

Cumberland 14, 22, 33, 44, 55, 58, 61, 71, 75, 77, 111
   Holme Cultram 48

Denbighshire 20, 26, 40
   Wrexham 21

Derbyshire 14, 23, 34, 44, 48, 61, 77, 84
   Chesterfield 23
   Derby 68
   Wirksworth 34

Derbyshire, North West 34

Devon 14, 23, 34, 44, 49, 55, 57, 58, 63, 65, 70, 74, 76, 93, 95, 105, 114
   Barnstaple 14
   Dartmoor 114
   Exeter 65, 78
   Hartland 34
   Plymouth 14, 34, 62, 78
   Shirwell 60
   South Hams 34
   Stoke Rivers 60
   Torbay 14
   Torquay 14

Devon, Southwest 34

Dorset 14, 23, 34, 44, 49, 58, 63, 67, 76, 87, 103, 111, 112
   Poole 34, 44

Durham 12, 14, 23, 24, 33, 34, 44, 56, 61, 70, 83, 90, 116
   Durham Diocese 12
   Easington 34
   Houghton le Spring 34
   Stockton 34

Essex 14, 23, 34, 44, 53, 55, 70, 76, 101
   Earls Colne 35, 57
   Grays 23

Newham 14
Redbridge 14
Waltham Forest 14

Flintshire 21, 26, 40
   Saint Asaphs Diocese 51

Glamorganshire 21, 26, 40, 56, 68, 74, 95
   Cardiff 40, 62, 95
   Cwmgors 61
   Swansea 13, 95

Glamorganshire, West 21

Gloucestershire & Bristol 14, 23, 35, 37, 44, 49, 58, 64, 75, 88, 112
   Bristol 14, 15, 23, 35, 70, 103
   Cotswolds 35
   Forest of Dean 35, 78
   Hawkesbury 35
   Randwick 35

Guernsey 20, 39, 54, 82, 95

Hampshire 15, 23, 35, 44, 64, 65, 76, 91, 116
   Isle of Wight 15, 35, 44, 68, 88
   Portsmouth 15
   Southampton 15
   Stubbington 61

Herefordshire 15, 23, 35, 44, 78, 112
   Bromyard 68

Hertfordshire 9, 15, 23, 35, 44, 58, 61, 68, 84
   Royston 23

Huntingdonshire 15, 23, 35, 44, 70, 78, 103

Isle of Man 20, 26, 39, 46, 61

Jersey 39, 51, 54, 62

Kent 9, 15, 23, 35, 36, 38, 44, 58, 70, 75, 78, 106, 109, 111, 114, 116
   Bexley 15
   Bromley 15
   Canterbury 70
   Folkestone 23
   Greenwich 15
   Lewisham 15
   Maidstone 56, 57, 84
   Ramsgate 95

Snodland 91
Tunbridge Wells 23

Kent, North West 23

Lancashire 15, 23, 36, 45, 57, 58, 71, 106, 115
Accrington 47
Blackburn 36
Bolton 15
Bury 16
Darwen 36
Furness 23
Lancaster 23
Liverpool 23, 45, 64, 67, 89, 91, 103
Manchester 16, 23, 45, 64, 97
North Meols 23
Oldham 16
Ormskirk 23
Rochdale 16, 64
Saint Helens 23
Salford 16
Salford Diocese 15
Salford Hundred 36
Southport 23
Tameside 9, 16, 36
Trafford 16
Walton 84
Wigan 16

Lancashire, South West 23

Leicestershire 16, 24, 36, 45, 61, 71, 73, 75

Lincolnshire 9, 16, 24, 36, 45, 57, 61, 68, 71, 74, 75, 81, 84, 100, 107
Cleethorpes 47
Grimsby 47
Isle of Axholme 24

Lincolnshire, South 22

London & Middlesex 9, 16, 24, 36, 45, 48, 51, 53-60, 62, 63, 67, 68, 71, 73-76, 78, 81-84, 87-92, 100, 101, 103, 104-106, 116
Brent 16
Camden 16
Cheapside 57
Chelsea 17, 68, 74
Christs Hospital 74
Cripplegate Ward 90
Ealing 16

Enfield 16
Fulham 17
Grey Friars 49
Hackney 17, 60
Hammersmith 17
Haringey 17
Harrow 17
Hillingdon 17
Honey Lane. All Hallows 57
Hounslow 17
Hyde Park 11
Islington 17
Kensington 17
Newgate 85
Poplar 74
Saint Martin in the Fields 74
Saint Martin Pomary 57
Saint Mary Colechurch 57
Saint Mary Le Bow 57
Saint Pauls Cathedral 49, 71, 74
Soper Lane. Saint Pancras 57
Tower Hamlets 17
Westminster 17, 65, 67, 76

Merionethshire 26, 40, 41

Monmouthshire 21, 26, 41

Montgomeryshire 21, 26, 41, 59, 72, 73
Machynlleth 77

Norfolk 17, 24, 36, 37, 45, 52, 58, 59, 65, 71, 73, 88, 103, 105, 115
Great Yarmouth 17
Kings Lynn 17
Norwich 17

Norfolk, Mid 24

Norfolk, West 22

Northamptonshire 17, 24, 37, 45, 47, 71
Peterborough 24

Northumberland 17, 24, 33, 37, 45, 61, 70, 116
Berwick upon Tweed 17
Gateshead 14
Newcastle 17
North Tyneside 17

Nottinghamshire 17, 24, 37, 45, 49, 59, 61, 73, 78, 104

Nottingham 67, 78
Southwell 68

Oxfordshire 17, 24, 37, 45, 49, 59, 73, 91
Oxford. Balliol College 13, 100
Ploughley Hundred 58

Pembrokeshire 21, 41, 111

Radnorshire 21, 26, 41

Rutland 17, 24, 37, 45, 71, 75

Sark 39

Shropshire 18, 24, 37, 45, 47, 72, 73, 88, 116
Stottesden Hundred 75

Somerset 18, 24, 35, 37, 45, 49, 58, 59, 63, 72, 78, 112
Bath 18
Bridgwater 95
Ilchester 18, 85
Weston super Mare 24

Somerset, North 37

Staffordshire 9, 13, 18, 24, 25, 37, 38, 45, 47, 72, 74, 78, 85, 92, 106, 116
Audley 24
Black Country 38
Burntwood 24
Burslem 72
Burton 18
Cotton 74
Stafford 108
Stoke on Trent 92
Tamworth 13
Tipton 24
Walsall 18, 24, 89
Wednesbury 24
Wolverhampton 18

Suffolk 9, 18, 25, 38, 45, 46, 72, 83, 107, 112, 116
Babergh Hundred 62
Blythburgh 49
Boxford 52
Bury St. Edmunds 18, 49, 55
Butley 49
Clare 49
Cratfield 52

Suffolk (*continued*)
Dodnash 49
Dunwich 62
Eye 49
Haverhill 25
Ipswich 18, 57, 62, 68, 72, 73
Leiston 49
Lowestoft 18
Sibton 49
Southwold 55
Stoke by Clare 49
Sudbury 49
Sudbury Archdeaconry 72
Walsham le Willows 57

Suffolk, South 53

Surrey 9, 18, 25, 38, 46, 57, 64, 71, 72, 116
Camberley 64
Croydon 18
Epsom 25
Godalming 74
Lambeth 18
Merton 18
Reigate 25
Richmond upon Thames 18
Sutton 18
Wandsworth 18

Sussex 9, 18, 25, 38, 46, 65, 67, 72, 78, 106, 112
Billingshurst 60
Eastbourne 25
Hastings 25
Weald 38

Sussex, West 75

Wales 9, 20, 26, 29, 39, 46, 54, 64, 65, 74, 80, 88, 91, 95, 104, 106, 112

Wales, North 51

Warwickshire 19, 25, 37, 38, 46, 47, 76, 85, 116
Birmingham 19, 38, 99
Coventry 19, 78, 81, 85
Rugby 25
Stratford upon Avon 19
Warwick 58

Westmorland 14, 19, 22, 33, 38, 44, 46, 51, 61, 71, 79, 111

Kendal 49

Wiltshire 19, 25, 37, 38, 46, 49, 58, 64, 67, 72, 73, 75, 112
Salisbury 91
Swindon 19

Worcestershire 19, 25, 37, 39, 46, 47, 58, 59, 72, 75, 76, 116
Badsey 39, 52
Bromsgrove 66
Dudley 19
Malvern 25

Yorkshire 13, 19, 25, 39, 46, 49, 57, 61, 64, 71, 75, 106, 112, 114, 115, 117
Barnsley 19, 25, 67
Bradford 19, 25
Calderdale 19, 25
Conisbrough 61
Dale Dyke 57
Doncaster 19, 25
East Riding 19, 55
Halifax 56
Harrogate 64
Huddersfield 25
Hull 12, 19, 62
Keighley 25
Kingston upon Hull 19
Kirklees 19
Knaresborough 46
Leeds 19, 20, 47
Morley 25
Pontefract 25
Ripon 25
Rotherham 20, 25
Sheffield 20, 26, 57
Wakefield 19, 26, 48, 61, 67, 76
West Riding 55
Wharfedale 26
York 9, 20, 26, 63, 72
York Diocese 19
York Minster 20

Yorkshire, East 25

Yorkshire, North 19

Yorkshire, West 19

OVERSEAS
Argentina 104

Australia 7, 29, 51, 84, 85, 102, 104, 115
New South Wales 85, 104

Austria 21

Bermuda 84

Canada 29, 104, 104, 107
Ontario 104
Ottawa 22
Quebec 66

Chile 104

Europe 100

France 22

Germany 22

Gibraltar 84

Hong Kong 99

India 11, 102

Italy 22, 30

Jamaica 51

Japan 92

Malaysia
Changi 92

Malta 104

New Zealand 26, 66, 104

South Africa 29, 66, 104

South America 29, 104

Spain
Trafalgar 96

United States 8, 22, 42, 66, 83, 85, 104, 105, 108
91 69
New England 66, 104, 109
New York 66
New York, Ellis Island 105

West Indies 85